EARTH MEDICINE :
A FIELD GUIDE

healing in seasons and cycles

By

Merrill Page

merrill@earthmedicineafieldguide.com

merrillpage.com

Published by EARTH MEDICINE INSTITUTE TAOS

The author of this book does not dispense medical advice or prescribe the use of any technique as a form of treatment for physical, emotional, or medical problems without the advice of a physician, either directly or indirectly. The intent of the author is only to offer information of a general nature to help you in your quest for emotional and physical well-being. In the event you use any of the information in this book for yourself, the author and the publisher assume no responsibility for your actions.

First Edition

Earth Medicine Institute Taos is an independent nonprofit organization devoted to advancing how Alternative Medicine is perceived, understood, and practiced. Through the production of written materials and classes, they seek to create a framework that unites individuals and practitioners in their mission to redefine and reclaim *medicine* for our times.

ISBN-13: 978-0-578-88766-1   Printed in USA

Cover design by Eli Marmar

Cover art by Daren Magee

Author photo by Stefanie Schwartz

Interior design by Tracy Atkins

Watermark art by Oliver DeVito

For you, for me,

For our children

ACKNOWLEDGEMENTS

This book would not exist without the love and devotion of a great number of people who stepped up and into it with me. Thank you Lauren Johnson for your unwavering commitment and attention to every detail. Kate Joss, for letting every word echo through you and finding new ones to beam back at me. Thank you Eli Marmar, for your guide work in the visual realms, for helping me find Daren. Daren Magee, for your brilliant illustration of the hard to see and touch layers. Tracy Atkins for putting the pieces together, and Carly Ball for starting them. Gustavo Actis Piazza, who always appears in the most miraculous moments, including now to offer his expert translation into Spanish. Micaela Heekin, Anne Bunn, Alexis Cohen, Amy Novesky and Dara Colacchio, for the hours you spent reading the early versions and encouraging me on. My children, Oliver, Rafa, Remi, and Alexei, who fed each word in their earnest and heartful experience of life. Without you, nothing. The family who birthed me, my beliefs, my privilege to know and to have lived so many diverse experiences across the planet. You are the soil that my words and visions stand on. Finally, the magical beings in my life who have brought the mystery to me and to this manuscript.

Thank you.

Contents

INTRODUCTION

"You know, the doctors of the future are going to be able to listen to your symptoms and direct you to the right kind of medicine…Acupuncture, herbs, Somatic therapy, Craniosacral therapy, Yoga," Catherine said. Just to name a few. Then she said, "Happy Birthday," and raised her glass to me.

It was my thirtieth, and we were celebrating at the Japanese Tea house in the Ferry Building on the Embarcadero in San Francisco. Here, sitting across from me, was Catherine Grey, the director of the then-nonprofit The Natural Step. Her eyes sparkled with mischief as she tried to remember her thirties and distill her memories into a single soundbite that could offer me a gift of understanding about what it means to be crossing this threshold into a new decade.

What she didn't realize was that her gift had already been given—a new vision for the doctors of the future.

Catherine was a leader. A visionary. An artist. A mother. She commanded the respect of both people and institutions, from the most modest to the most powerful. And her *presence* was as intuitive, fluid, and relational as her *mind* was keen, discerning, and incisive. Catherine had the ability to listen, digest what was said, and then offer back incredible insights. She had the ability to hold the gaze and respect of a huge conference room filled with people eager to hear about trends in big business and their long-term implications for future health on the planet, both individual and ecological.

But on this day, Catherine was speaking to me alone when she said, "There's a trip I have always wanted to do," she said. "But I never had the right person to go with. Until now. Come on!! Let's go."

So, I went.

Three weeks later we were in Ecuador, traveling with the PachaMama Alliance into a remote area of the Amazon to learn about the Medicine of the Achuar people.

Being there was medicine unto itself. There was no sense of being "away" from anything, but rather a feeling of being home, and at the heart of it all, even with our loved ones and our livelihoods thousands of miles away.

The dynamic of the group of travelers was held and facilitated by David Tucker, another natural born leader and, like Catherine, a healer unto himself. David's listening, reflections, curiosity, and masculine strength wove us together in a dis-armed, open, and intimate way, where healing could take place within a field of trust and ease. Relational dynamics re-patterned themselves there, and we learned entire new ways of being.

There was also the Shaman and his medicine, which is so multi-layered and contextual that only pieces of it will be revealed in this book. And to receive them, you may have to read it many times to notice them, to taste, and then digest what it is that a well-trained Shaman offers to his people.

The rainforest expresses the purest form of Earth Medicine. There are plants, roots, flowers, branches, trees, and ecosystems that have co-existed with each other and amongst a group of people and their culture since the beginning of time. Each piece of the earth becomes known, revered, and employed to transform illness to wellness, disease to health, and separation to connection.

Medicine is offered in ceremony with reverence for the spirit of the plant and the privilege of taking its medicine. Healing happens within the context of relationship. That's just how it is. There is relationship to the natural world and its plants and animals, to the elements, to each other, to ourselves, and even to our ancestors, and what we still carry for them. Healing cannot be separated from this, just as the winding, in-folding, and out-folding among species of the rainforest cannot be lined up, contained, and made linear or separate.

So tightly woven is the ecosystem in the rainforest that the food for our travels had to be flown in with us from our world. To eat fish from their river or fruits from their trees would upset the local balance between humans and fauna. As much as it pained me not to eat what was there in the landscape, I felt great relief in this awareness and in the commitment to respecting their balance.

Here in the rainforest everything is gendered, and the continuation of life forms depends on each expressing his/her masculine and feminine qualities. It is the Male:Female, Light:Dark, Active:Receptive states of being that allows for fertility and the birth of new forms. New life depends on the polarity of opposites, and it was in the context of this interdependency of life that we came to see the possibility of our own wholeness.

Modern life is now far removed from these organic forms of culture and integrated medicine. But echoes, vibrations, lessons, and even rare embodiments of these endangered forms of living and healing still remain. They offer us a blueprint for how to proceed and a trail of crumbs to help us find our way back to our relationship with true Earth Medicine.

I brought back from the jungle not only my reverence for plant medicine and how it is practiced inside of ceremony, culture, and a local landscape, but also a deeper sense of my own heart and my own humility. My mind finally surrendered to an awareness that Spirit holds a much greater command over life than any of my choices or desires, and in the end it must be served.

So, after years of telling myself I would not bring children into a world so off-target, I had four. I finally relinquished myself to becoming part of the tangle of life, despite the inevitable future of loss, grief, global warming, mass extinctions, abuses of power, systemic failures of leadership across disciplines, and the impossibility of what I would be leaving my children.

I have been led through the complexities and impossibilities, time and time again, by the role model of the Latina Mama. She is the truest embodiment of *heart* and *humility* that I have found. I think of *her* as an archetype that I aspire to and measure myself against when the present is too painful to bare, and the future is dark and unwelcome.

I met her in my childhood, traveling through Spain as a girl of 12 years. She was in the kitchen, in the music, in the house cleaning the cobwebs at the same time she delighted in knowing her man would be home at the end of the day. She was in the dialectic between the notes pouring out of the gypsy's nylon-stringed guitar and the fierce, passionate stomping of the flamenco shoes on a hardwood floor. I found her again in my young adult years living in South America and in their literature. She was the woman who stayed home with her child and felt fulfilled by that. And the one who ran away, driven wild by her own fire and cooled only by the pursuit of her passion. Every female archetype in Laura Esquivel's *Like Water for Chocolate* captured my imagination for what "woman" is and how her longings play out or get played, according to her circumstances, and her courage to meet her own heart.

So I learned how to mother in Spanish. It's where my softness comes from as well as my fierce and unapologetic strength. The Spanish/Latina Mama, for me, was feminine, full-bodied, and fierce. She was the goddess not only of her own hunger, but of her home, and of her kitchen. She was articulate in the ingredients of what it is to hold a family in a feminine way, to respond to her man in a sensuous, embodied, and receptive way, and to build a beautiful, layered, abundant meal filled with heart, and tradition, for her often large and hungry family.

And so, she is my heroine.

Here, at the crossroads of mass extinction and privileged models for living that have not served even the people who are living within them, I call on her again. Can the heart and humility of what is modeled by the most modest women on the planet, the women who give themselves daily to seeding, feeding, watering, educating, shuttling, clothing, and caring for their children, often without a dime to their names, serve as a model for us now?

INTRODUCTION

On the heels of crisis and quarantine, a global pandemic and a merciless virus, we have all been cracked open to new levels of vulnerability. It is here, when we are most broken and in need of grace, that the clouds in our eyes may lift so we may find the willingness to step onto a new path.

What are the steps we can take to make our homes safe again? The home in our bodies. The home in our houses. The home on this planet.

What is the true medicine for the time we live in? A time where we are crippled—not only by viruses like Covid-19 and poisonous plants like poison oak—but also by our beliefs about how to treat these things, and how to treat ourselves?

This book offers new archetypes and a new kind of heroine to show us the way.

In addition to offering you my own love for Latin culture and the spiritual heroes and heroines who keep the flame of the hearth and the seeds of their gardens alive, I offer you my lifelong passion for alternatives to medicine. Some are grounded into my lived experiences with people who still walk the earth, literally, harvesting and making medicine as they go. Others come from a lifelong study in Alternative and Complementary Medicine, received by the most educated and articulate in the field of their personal and professional studies.

Here, they come as stories, stories that reflect what it is to actually embody hunger, failure, and self-denial, then permission, fulfillment, understanding, and loss again. The stories show what it is to live out the impulses of each element—earth, water, fire, air, and ether—and to dance in and out of imbalance with each one.

Life as a balance and embodiment of the Natural Elements is a timeless concept served up to us by ancient cultures and systems of medicine, from Persia and ancient Arabic Alchemical Medicine to Greece and European pre-French Clinical Scientific Practice. China to India had their own tools and maps as did each local Indigenous tribe seeking balance and harmony for both individuals and the group as a whole as they moved in and out of health. Each one, though separated by time and space, acknowledged health as a fluid, unfolding and infolding process of life seeking balance through the Elements as they manifest within us.

We bring this idea, that health is fluid and cyclical, back to life here. I choose the Medicine Wheel, which is Indigenous to my place and the roots I seek to know here on this land, as my tool. It is the organizational principle that guides me through the process of loss and letting go, then reclamation and deep introspection, which is the cyclical process of losing health, then regaining it.

So there are stories, poems, soundbites we call quotes, and recipes. The recipes, too, pay homage to the awareness that just as life seeks harmony between the Elements and the nature of each one, so do our meals. Chinese Medicine and Ayurvedic Medicine both knew this and used food as medicine to restore balance. The food was combined and prepared in just the right way to balance not just flavor and digestive ease, but also the elemental constitution brought forth by each food. In many cases the concept of medicine and food were never separate. The recipes here emerge from that premise.

The idea of nourishment goes deeper though. Today, most of us reading this book have the infinite privilege of choosing what to eat or not eat. We hunger more for adventure, experience, love, and a sense of purpose. The essays in this book are written to bring us home to that—the awareness that what we hunger for goes much deeper than what we put on our plates and depends more fully on others than many of us want to believe.

Come feast, page by page, on words, thoughts, ideas. Ageless tools and storied elements, new archetypes and shared echoes called poetry, here to pierce your heart of its illusions. Your heart, like everything, must be ruptured open for you to see what's inside. Only then can you glimpse the possibility of sharing what's there. It is in the sharing, of who you are and what you are here to bring, that the wellspring of your joy, your freedom, and your health reside.

GUIDING PRINCIPLES

The list below in no way summarizes all of the many choices there are today in the field of Complementary and Alternative Medicine, but it succinctly defines the terms used in this book. It also introduces some key concepts you'll find woven throughout the text. I hope you will come back to this section, again and again, for orientation and insight into the world of medicine that awaits you.

Acupuncture - Acupuncture is a science and an art form that dates back thousands of years in China. It regards the body as a physical manifestation of the elements—wood, fire, earth, metal, and water—and maps their currents onto the human body. Dis-ease in the body and the mind are treated equally, and the body is viewed as a map where energetic forces step down into physical matter. Needles are applied to specific points on the body to open energy currents where they are stuck. The release of energy restores life force and health when it is absent. Acupuncture is based on a cyclical model of relationships between the five elements listed in Chinese Medicine.

Anthroposophy - Anthroposophy is a philosophy pioneered by Rudolf Steiner, a revolutionary thinker of the early 20th century. It is based on an integrated view of the human being where spiritual, emotional, psychological, and physical aspects of one's self are perceived and regarded with equal weight and importance. It has inspired multiple applications in diverse fields including education (Waldorf Schools), business, agriculture, and medicine. Anthroposophical medicine, one application of anthroposophy, is a holistic form of medicine that seeks to address physical, psychological, and spiritual symptoms of health with equal attention and within a social context.

Ayurveda - Both a science and an art, Ayurveda is a form of medicine whose roots date back 2,000 years ago in India. It considers both the interior constitution and humor of an individual, as well as the exterior climate and elements in which the person lives, when assessing health. In Ayurveda, remedies can include food, lifestyle, herbs, and daily/seasonal ritual. A keystone principle in Ayurveda is *good digestion = good health*.

Biodynamic - This word, commonly applied to a form of agriculture called biodynamic farming, suggests that the healthy biological unfolding of an ecosystem requires attention to the harmonics and integration of all factors of growth, including moon cycles, diversity in a natural ecosystem, and non-toxic solutions to pest management. It is a concept growing in popularity as both mainstream and organic farms seek new solutions to old problems in supply and demand. New science that links health and illness to chemical fertilizers and pesticides in food supplies encourages the expansion of biodynamic thought in food production.

Bodymind - The word bodymind refers to the continuous entity of one's being, where the mind deposits itself into the cells and gives shape to the physical body. This term, while a beautiful metaphor, can also be interpreted literally. Our felt experiences are registered in the body on a cellular level. Psychoneuroimmunology, a relatively new form of allopathic medicine, and Somatic therapy both spring from this concept that our minds and bodies are united in form and must be addressed together to achieve full recovery in health. Older pre-Cartesian forms of medicine such as Ayurveda and Chinese Medicine are already founded on this principle of the united bodymind.

Chakras - Centers of energy and consciousness where energy spirals down from invisible planes and into the body. The major chakras are located on specific points along the North-South pole from the crown to the base of the body, but there are hundreds of other minor chakras located on the surface of the body.

Chi - A term used in Chinese Medicine to describe the energy in exchange in our daily actions and interactions. It is pure energy that is stored in the heart and solar plexus, the name for the area just above your bellybutton and below your breastplate. Chi also runs through the meridians and therefore feeds or impacts the emotional body. Chi regulates the immune/endocrine/neurological systems. It is accumulated or increased through love and engagement with true passion and interests.

Chinese Medicine - Chinese Medicine has been applied and refined for more than 2,000 years and currently refers to medicinal practices that emphasize nutritional and herbal remedies as well as bodily treatments, including Acupuncture, moxa, Qigong healing, and cupping. It is based on the principles of relationship between five elemental entities: wood, fire, earth, metal, and water. They are represented in a circle of relationships to show which element nourishes and which element controls the other. There is a nourishing cycle that moves in a circle and reflects the Mother-Child relationship. It is known as the Shen cycle. Then, there is a controlling cycle known as the Ko cycle and said to reflect the Brother-Sister relationship.

Craniosacral Therapy (Cranial Work) - Craniosacral therapy is hands-on therapeutic practice pioneered by doctor of osteopathic medicine William Sutherland, DO and furthered by John Upledger DO. It is now practiced by osteopaths and bodyworkers worldwide. CST employs subtle touch to support profound shifts in both the neuromusculoskelatal system and the subtle (energetic) body. Though still considered alternative to conventional medical practice, patients and practitioners marvel at its power to release pain from the body and alleviate symptoms in the nervous, immune, and endocrine systems. CST can be applied to relieve stress, fatigue, insomnia, indigestion, infertility, depression, and anxiety as well as trauma including birth trauma, infant colic and feeding difficulties.

Cryotherapy - Cryotherapy is newer on the list of alternative treatments, but ancient as a practice of self-care. In Cryotherapy, an individual submerges his/her complete body into close to freezing temperatures, like an ice-bath or an ice cold stream. It is thought to relieve muscle pain, support restoration in cases of injury, reduce inflammation, improve mental health, and treat migraine headaches.

Doula - A birth attendant, separate from a nurse or midwife, who partners with the mother during birth and acts as an advocate in communicating the mother's desires, wants, and needs during and just after the birth.

Flower Essences - Flower essences are a form of Homeopathy, or vibrational medicine, that treat imbalances or blocks in the spiritual-emotional fields. In countries like Germany and Argentina, they are sold alongside prescription medicine in pharmacies. Here in the U.S., practitioners are still trying to "prove" their efficacy in improving moods and emotional states.

Homeopathy - Homeopathy means "like cures like." It is based on the principle that an element in nature that holds similar qualities to an ailment will be the cure for that person. Homeopathic Medicine can be applied as first-aid to address symptoms of fever, bee stings, rashes, headaches, nausea, bruising, and diarrhea, to name a few. Or as a constitutional remedy, where one remedy mirrors the essential nature of an individual and is given to him no matter what he is suffering. Doses are given in highly diluted forms to trigger a healing response on the level of vibration. They can be taken many times throughout the day with no toxic side effects. Homeopathic medicine is a wonderful form of care for children.

I Ching - The I Ching is believed to be the oldest book in the Chinese culture and was compiled in the Chou Dynasty by Confucian philosophers. It is based on symbolic figures called trigrams. They are symbols that lay the foundation for theory in Qigong, Tai qi, Chinese Medicine, Feng Shui, and other ancient systems which use the relationship of the elements as a framework for their theoretical practices. In the I Ching, the trigrams are paired in twos to create a hexagram which shows the movement and relationship between yin and yang, feminine and masculine, dark and light. At the same time, they are symbols for Earth, Water, Fire, Wind, Heaven, Thunder, Mountain, and Lake—each of the natural elements and their variations. It is in these relationships that we find 64 potential states of being. And so, we have a map for the multitude of experiences that are possible when we relate—as human beings, as male and female, as manifestations of the elements, and as people in families, in groups, and in society.

Intuition Medicine - This term refers to a school of alternative medicine founded by Francesca McCartney PhD to train professionals in Medical Intuition. Integrating scientific research with stringent protocols for tracking and working with intuitive sciences, McCartney outlines maps of the energy body and teaches how we use them to treat medical conditions both in ourselves and in others. Much of the work is done through the practice of grounding, meaning bringing your awareness and energy into your physical body and down into the ground, and through awareness of and treatment through the chakras.

Jing - A term used in Chinese Medicine to refer to the deepest source of energy in the physical body, pure essence. It is stored in the lower abdomen—womb space (real or symbolic)—and believed to be our inherited and genetically gifted well of energy. It regulates sexual organs in the body. Jing comes from earth/nature. Jing, when it is low, can be increased or restored by the right food and drink as well as energy practices such as Qigong.

Medicine Shield – When I use the term Medicine Shield, I refer to each stop along the wheel—the South, the West, the North, and the East—where an individual arrives to meet the teachings therein. They are explained in depth in Chapter One of the book. A shield is where we come to know our strengths, powers, true gifts, and forms of protection that we must learn to embody in any given stage of life.

Medicine Wheel - The Medicine Wheel is an ancient tool used by countless Indigenous peoples and tribes to organize and explain the processes of growth and evolution—both cyclically throughout life and in life as a whole. It gives us a framework for understanding ourselves as well as our health/medicine as a process. The completion of each step through the shield leads to a claiming of one's true power, gifts, and understanding, both for ourselves and our people. The Medicine Wheel reflects the idea of a compass with cardinal directions and places the stages of growth: childhood, adolescence, adulthood, and elderhood in each cardinal point of the wheel: South, West, North, and East. In the process of becoming, we cycle clockwise, up from the south and down into the east.

Naturopathic Medicine - Naturopathic Medicine puts nature at the center of its philosophy and practice, and it employs techniques from multiple schools of medicine including diet, herbs, lifestyle, exercise, bodywork, energy work, and homeopathy as well as ancient systems such as Ayurveda and Chinese Medicine. Naturopathic physicians complete training in biological sciences as well as the rigors of pre-medical students including physics, chemistry, and basic anatomical science. Naturopathic medicine can be seen as a bridge between allopathic medicine (conventional means to treat symptoms or disease) and alternative forms of healing. Naturopathic physicians are now even compensated through insurance in some States.

Pilates – This form of movement, embraced by dancers, athletes, and now mainstream individuals seeking balance in fitness, helps one connect with and engage core muscles while strengthening, elongating, and healing bodily systems. Pioneered by visionary Joseph Pilates, it uses his specific equipment and techniques to achieve whole body health through movement.

Plant Spirit Medicine - Plant Spirit Medicine is a newer term used in herbal medicine to refer to the use of whole plants and the importance of considering the animus, or spirit, of a plant when making and receiving medicine. This term applies to the use of plants as medicine in many forms, including teas, tinctures, capsules, salves, topical compresses, smokes, and ceremony. In extreme cases, Ayahuasca and Peyote are believed to facilitate transcendental states and spiritual transformation.

Polarity Therapy – This therapy was pioneered and designed by Doctor Randolph Stone who perceived the body as an ecosystem where the elements earth, water, fire, air, and ether exist in balance. Though it draws its inspiration from diverse cultures and spiritual practices, it is deeply rooted in Ayurveda. Like Ayurveda, it offers herbs, nutrition, and lifestyle as pathways to wellness. But it goes on to employ hands-on techniques or gentle manipulations to the body in order to balance energy and restore health when it is blocked. Like Craniosacral therapy, it seeks to connect with the deep source of health or wellness already inside the body and draw light and healing from there.

Qigong - Qigong is the study and practice of cultivating energy *within* and *beyond* the body. It is based on the study of five elements in nature and lays the foundation for Tai Chi, Acupuncture, and Chinese Medicine.

Ritual - Ceremonial actions followed in sacred devotion and deep space as an act of reverence. Ritual facilitates connection to a spiritual reality where healing and transformation occur.

Sacred Geometry - A term used to refer to the geometrical patterns observed in snowflakes, crystals, sunflowers, and living matter throughout the natural world. Sacred Geometry bridges the ancient study of universal patterns with burgeoning physics on the harmonics and repetitions of the natural world. The positive impact of Sound therapy, Vibrational therapy, and other forms of homeopathic medicine would attribute its success to the invisible matrix woven in space that carries these harmonic resonant patterns.

Shamanism - Shamanism is the term we apply to the ancient, earth-based practices once used as medicine in Indigenous cultures across the globe. The Shaman is the Medicine Man, and he/she uses a variety of tools including ritual, rhythm and drumming, plant medicine, divine guidance, spirit and plant guides, metaphor, prayer, visualization, and food and herbal preparations as cures for patients across a broad spectrum of disease, including spiritual, psychological, emotional, and physical.

Shen - In Qigong theory and practice, and the Chinese Medicine that follows it, Shen is the energy of the Spirit. It is closely associated with the heart, but directly influenced by consciousness, the mind, our thoughts, and visual images. Shen is believed to be stored in the third eye, a symbolic point between our eyebrows. It is fed by Chi, as well as by Spiritual practice or Spirit work, in any of its diverse forms including prayer, the study of ancient texts, Qigong, consciousness studies, meditation, forgiveness practices, ritual, time in nature, and practices of self-transformation.

Somatic Therapy - Somatic therapy is a form of psychotherapy based on the belief that our stories and narratives are held in our bodies. To release trauma and limiting thoughts or memories, we take our attention to the body and to the breath and intend release of the cellular memories held there. The term Somatic therapy is also used to refer to diverse forms of therapeutic practices beyond psychotherapy including meditation and energy work such as Polarity therapy and Craniosacral therapy.

Spanish/Latina Mama - Here I use both words, Spanish and Latina, to describe my archetypal heroine who uses Spanish as her mother tongue. Yet the cultures of those who live in Spain, those who live in Central America, and those who live in South America are different, and they ask to be defined separately. Their diverse roots are as unique as the tender gifts they bring to their homes, and, though I generalize with the term Spanish/Latina, I am deeply aware of the native practices these women carry through. Here in my narrative, *she* is the women who gave me Spanish as a language to mother in. *She* showed me to embody a strength, character, and a maternal instinct that is as tender and attentive as it is protective and fierce.

Storytelling as Medicine - How we construct stories and narratives is as essential to our reality and health as anything we eat or take in. They are the frameworks for how we see the world as well as the foundation for how we think and, underneath that, what we believe. So, storytelling is a way of finding the way. It lays down archetypes, heroes and heroines, and possible conflict and resolution into images and words that instruct us on how to see and how to think. Storytelling then, is an essential piece of healing or medicine. Re-constructing our own stories about what we have lived or have seen can help us navigate obstacles, overcome blockages, and create new solutions and visions for the future.

Therapeutic Touch - A form of energy work founded by nurse practitioner Dolores Krieger that uses universal energy and directed intention to restore balance in the bodymind. Here, gentle interventions influence multiple levels of health, including spiritual, emotional, and physical. Since the 1970s, controlled scientific experiments have been implemented to measure and quantify the biochemical effects of such work on the human field. Therapeutic touch is now taught in over 100 countries and practiced by over 200,000 individuals.

Visualization - Visualization is a technique employed in doctors' offices and Yoga classes alike to help an individual center and find resources in challenging moments. It asks you to look inside for an image, thought, voice, sound, or memory that brings a sense of peace and calm. Visualization can be used to reduce stress and the illnesses caused and exacerbated by stress on biological or physiological levels. Visualization techniques are a central part of Intuition Medicine and assist one in bringing his/her energy both down into the ground for stronger embodiment, and down into the body for a clear sense of self in relationship to other.

Yoga - Yoga is believed to date back to the origins of the Vedas, which are the spiritual texts at the heart of Ayurveda. It employs postures and meditations to open the spine and overall body and support health on a physical, emotional, and spiritual level. It can be vigorous and athletic or quiet and restorative. Yoga postures can even be employed to restore health on the organ level.

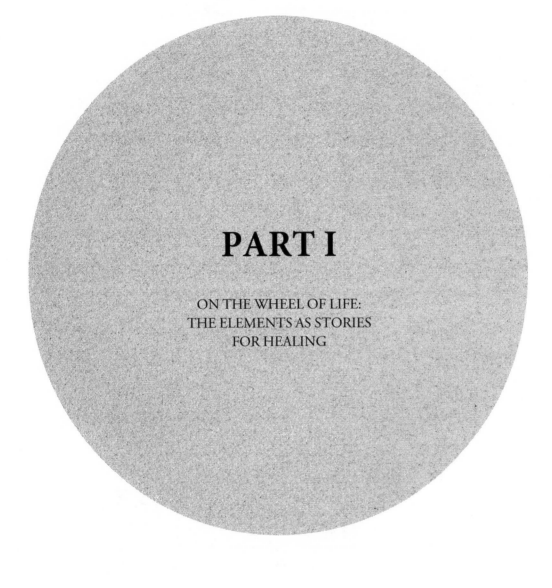

PART I

ON THE WHEEL OF LIFE:
THE ELEMENTS AS STORIES
FOR HEALING

CHAPTER ONE

THE MEDICINE WHEEL

Male/Female Medicine

The Medicine Wheel embodies the concept that all life is interconnected and interdependent. It symbolizes the holy sequences we move through in birth/life/death cycles throughout our entire lives. It is the space created by the shape of a circle, to show us the concept of a continuum and the ongoing and infinite processes that unfold throughout the journey of one's life.

For centuries across the globe, the Medicine Wheel was a tool that Shamans brought as 'doctors' to their communities to assist in rituals that facilitated a conscious movement through life/death cycles intended to restore health on multiple levels throughout the community. In these instances, the Medicine Wheel was not just a symbol. It was the literal creation of a structure marked usually with stones in four cardinal directions, with additional points between each one, to light the path of healing for the community, for the land they lived on, and for the individuals suffering within it. Shamans worked with the belief that manifested forms, such as a Medicine Wheel, echo into the other layers of our existence and awareness, and therefore hold the power to heal not just on a physical level, but on an emotional and spiritual level as well.

Today the Medicine Wheel is a symbol we can reclaim as a tool to help us find our own way. The linear structures applied in modern medicine are taxed beyond their capacity to serve. In addition, these current models only hold one piece of the complex mechanisms required to truly heal illness, relieve pain, and restore health. Missing is the round, circular, and relational piece of the Feminine model for health. The Feminine model is process-oriented, fluid, intuitive, and emphasizes the importance of moving in cycles toward a desired feeling or outcome. It is found in therapeutic modalities and hides behind old creaky doors in lost places, inside the tongues of languages that are no longer spoken in the modern world.

Like modern forms of medicine that are widely accepted and practiced today, these feminine ways of healing are also quantifiable, systematic, and stand up to rigors of scientific observation and trial. Diverse systems of therapy across the spectrum of modalities have, in fact, been analytically researching and "proving" their efficacy for decades already. The power of such models in healing is indisputable. It is time to put them back into the equation.

Together, the direct, corrective role of the masculine and the indirect, process-oriented role of the feminine approach to medicine form a complete picture of what we will need to restore health moving ahead. If we can find a way to fold them back together in mutual respect and rigor, we have hope for the future of medicine.

ARRIVING AT THE FUTURE, A FEMININE TAKE ON "ADULTING"

Arriving at adulthood is no small thing. And so, generations of diverse people across the planet have required coming of age rituals and rites of passage for their adolescents. There is something about being pushed to the edge of your discomfort in a ritual setting that awakens you to what you are truly capable of. Especially over an extended period of time, as was required in coming of age rituals within Indigenous tribes.

So while many of these traditional forms of ushering children into adulthood appear extreme to us as a modern people, they were essential to birthing the future adults of any given tribe, for they knew that experience cannot be replaced by anything. No school lesson, no conversation, no movie, no idea, no essay can give you the experience of living that thing, of feeling it, and of knowing it in your body. The body's lived experience is an essential piece in the construction of the biological systems and the mental frameworks that make up a human being. Our brains and neural pathways depend on our having the musculoskeletal and nervous imprint that comes from doing something.

So, arriving at or into adulthood is no small accomplishment, especially without a cultural mechanism to get you there. The more you know about who you are and what you are capable of *before* becoming an adult, the more equipped you are to meet the demands of being one.

"The sheer aliveness of a clear and instantaneous knowing is the cornerstone of one's true radiance and health." —**Richard Rudd** (*The Gene Keys*)

My "people" didn't require this kind of experiential rite-of-passage. The debutante party, "our" coming of age celebration, didn't require a process of separation, or moving across a threshold from one state of being to another. There was no teaching to help me understand what I was leaving and what now lay ahead. And so, I lost my way.

I learned to trust what I was told instead of what I felt to be real and true. The lack of ceremony and reverence for a person's deep self, their sexuality, and their true strengths, made the world I was supposed to step into undesirable.

I may have been too hungry for the things I was not allowed to have: sex, strength, fat, power.

So I stopped eating. We called it "anorexia" and treated it that way. With a rigorous regimen for gaining weight and many hours of talk therapy, I made my way from 99 pounds to the 115 pounds required to get me out of the danger zone and back onto the sports field. I was 13 years old.

But even with the best doctors, medical experts, and psychologists, none of us really understood just how I ended up in such a severe crisis, causing danger to myself, and heartbreak and estrangement to those who loved me.

I was deemed clinically healed at age 13, but by 20 had been diagnosed with amenorrhea, chronic fatigue syndrome, and Raynaud's disease. I had three dead teeth that required root canals, thinning hair and nails, and lanugo—a biological condition of excess hair on the body to help insulate it in cases of starvation or malnutrition. I was well on my way to infertility and digestive complications.

No matter how much I weighed or didn't weigh, the challenges remained. Those challenges were imprinted into my body, my emotions, and my beliefs about what was safe and what wasn't. I have spent many years untangling these thoughts and symptoms in order to find my way to true medicine.

I think, if I had been given a vision of Womanhood that I could embrace at age 13, the path may have been different. A vision that was round, fierce, fed, embodied. One where when you were pushed, you pushed back to meet the energy with equal strength and force. One where you listened, inside and out as well as moment to moment, in order to discern what was true, what was to be spoken, and what could remain silent. What was best to be taken in, or what should be kept outside of your boundary lines.

CLAIMING YOUR IDENTITY

Who am I, and what does that have to do with my health anyway?

The full embodiment and experience of health throughout our lives depends on growing up and one's sense of Identity when arriving. Our immune systems, our nervous systems, and our endocrine systems will all be influenced by how deeply we have delved into finding ourselves, knowing ourselves, claiming ourselves, and then finally coming back into the world with a secure hold on who we are—unapologetic in the truth of it. Not only do our identities depend upon this, but the energetic openness and integrity of the body and its systems of health depend on this: our ability to occupy our own space.

In the Shamanic perspective, health depends on one's soul being intact. It is offense to the soul that causes illness.

"It was nature, wildness, this undomesticated spirit that fled when it got enslaved, insulted, maimed, beaten or scared off. This trespass on one's personal nature or soul is what Mayan shamans considered the prime source of illness to humans." — **Martin Prechtel**

Homeopathic Medicine, which uses highly diluted forms of natural substances to treat physical conditions of imbalance, also recognizes that physical health cannot be separated from emotional well-being. Dr. Edward Bach, a respected physician, homeopath, and founder of flower essence therapy, pioneered this concept within the medical community in the 1920s and 1930s. "To create health, the emotional and spiritual aspects of our beings must be addressed," he insisted. "True health is based on a connection of one's life and destiny with a larger purpose" (Kaminski and Katz, 2004, *Flower Essence Repertory*). And so, a doctor of homeopathy seeks not only to treat acute symptoms of illness with his medicine, but to discover a constitutional remedy for his patient that, by mirroring an individual on his deepest level, remedies all symptoms, from headache to fever, from diarrhea to post-surgery recovery, from warts to indigestion, from depression to anger.

I have seen this work most miraculously with my oldest son, who was diagnosed by our naturopath as having a "phosphorous constitution." Often, when he is out of balance and angry, sore, congested, or sick, I will give him his "sugar balls" of phosphorous. The turnaround is swift and complete, and within an hour he is back in ease and flow.

Psychoneuroimmunology, a form of psychosomatic medicine established in the 1980s that has been gaining momentum and scientific relevance ever since, begins to measure the physical effects of our beliefs, attitudes, and feelings on our physiological systems, including the immune and endocrine systems. Rigorous, controlled, scientific study offers evidence for how—through biologic mechanisms—our beliefs interact with our feelings and how these feelings are chemically transmitted or imprinted onto our bodies, thus creating physical responses that become health or disease in the organism.

SEASONS, CYCLES, AND STAGES—THE PROCESS OF BECOMING HUMAN

When you allow or are allowed to pass with full embrace through each season of your life with authentic expression, then health and wellness will follow. Every stage is required for a person to become his/her fullest and most vibrant version of Self. This is a cyclical model. A feminine model. A model of aging that recognizes we come back, over and over again to the same themes.

Ideally, with each return, we bring new awareness. This awareness, which is merely a shift in consciousness, is at the heart of becoming an adult—that is, fully present in any stage of life, no matter how old you are. It can only happen when an experience is complete—meaning, fully lived through the body and fully felt through the heart.

"Why do so many adults dislike children?" Oliver, my 13 year old, asks me one day.

"Hmmm. Good question. I think it has something to do with losing touch of their own joy," I reply.

Rafa, my 10 year old, looks at me. He's not at all convinced. "I don't think so," he adds.

"Well," I said as I grasped for a response. "Why don't I ask you guys that question in 20 years and see what you have to say about it? I wonder what your answer will be?"

"Oliver will be 33 in 20 years," Rafa says.

"Perfect!" I said. "Thirty-three is the age Jesus was when he was crucified. It is an important age in becoming an adult."

It's interesting to note, there are also 33 bones in your spinal column.

The Medicine Wheel Points the Way

The Medicine Wheel, a tool given to us by Indigenous cultures, is surfacing again now in some alternative earth-based forms of therapy. It offers a model to understand the importance of every single stage and cycle of your life. This simple validation, and permission to move through each one, is healing unto itself. It gives space and acceptance for feelings and experiences. Once you know how you feel and simply feel it, you can let it go. It is a cyclical model for the phases we pass through—not just once, but over and over again on our journey from start to end, as we cycle through in a clockwise direction.

In its "macro" form it describes how we pass from youth, to adolescence, to adulthood, then finally to being an elder. Each direction on the cardinal map is said to embody one stage of life: South - youth, West - adolescence, North - adulthood, East - elderhood. They are described in depth below. In its "micro" form, each direction also points to phases we return to over and over in life, even as an adult or an elder.

I use the term "Medicine Shield" to refer to a single place inside of the wheel, one single direction. So, there is the Medicine Shield of the South, the Medicine Shield of the West, the Medicine Shield of the North, and the Medicine Shield of the East.

Each aspect of our growth depends on moving through these directions, fully and completely, in an embodied way.

1. South: the embodiment of summer, the potential joy and delight of the physical body

2. West: the embodiment of fall, where one turns inward to excavate one's deepest self and true gifts

3. North: the embodiment of winter, and assuming responsibility for what you have created, as an individual and as a community

4. East: the embodiment of spring, an illumination of consciousness, a deeper awareness of life spirit

Our health, which is linked to our fullest presence, depends on our embrace of each of these stages, over and over again.

Remember, each direction represents a stage of life.

Summer, symbolized in the **Southern** shield, is the embodiment of childhood, its joy and physicality, warmth and unself-conscious expression. It is a first stage of cyclical being and can be experienced as the most desired or happy of all, but it's not to be grasped at or held on to.

Questions to explore during the Summer seasons include:

What delights me?
How do I play?
What does life feel like? Taste like? Smell like?
How do I feed my hunger and express my strength?

The Southern shield is reflected in the formation and instinctual nature of the physical body. The focus of an unencumbered childhood is to simply discover and express this.

Turning one step clockwise we arrive in **Fall,** which is symbolized in the **Western** shield. This is a time of turning inward. It is associated with the adolescent and insists that, even while one is groping to understand his/her place in the bigger picture of one's group of peers, he/she must look inside for the deeper truths of identity and divine purpose. Here we take time to recognize our true superpowers and gifts.

Questions to explore during the Fall season include:

Who am I?
What do I stand for?
How am I strong?
How am I vulnerable?

These are all essential questions for the adolescent.

If summer and the Southern shield is about developing the physical body, this time of the fall and Western shield marks the formation of one's emotional body and emotional identity. It determines how each of us learns to meet the world from a state of feeling, rather than through pure physical contact or through mental interaction. The best way through this stage, like all of them, is to experience it with as much awareness and willingness as possible.

Turning clockwise again, we encounter the **Winter** of our lives. It lives in the **Northern** shield and is symbolic of adulthood: responsibility. Here, one claims authorship. Here, we strive to discover how we will serve the community at large.

Questions to explore during the Winter questions are:

What am I responsible for? … To?
What is my role in the group?
What is my work in the world?
How do I discipline myself to achieve it?

This role is as essential as the role of bringing joy to the world through our unselfconscious expression of childhood in the Southern shield. It must be claimed. We must stand up to and for our purpose in the world, our function as part of the whole. This will serve not only our sense of purpose and belonging, but our physical and emotional health as well. The action of 'claiming one's life' is the antidote to our addictions, depression, emotional longings, or landmines.

If the Southern shield is a physical experience, and the Western shield is an emotional one, then the Northern shield is a mental experience and deals with the development of the mind.

Finally, if each phase is embraced and experienced to its fullest, then accepted and released, we move into the symbolic season of **Spring**, the **Eastern** shield. This is symbolized and embodied by our wise elders. It is a place of light, surrender, and holding space as a witness for the actions expressed in each of the other shields. It is the place of illumination and of pure spirit. It is the home of one's intuition. It offers the gift of insight and of creativity.

Here there is little action, and one is invited to sit in wonder asking mostly:

What is?

Ultimately, illumination is the shift in consciousness that knows "all is well." Your purpose has been expressed. Your needs have been met. Life becomes a gesture of love and deep inner peace.

The Medicine Wheel has been a treasured tool among earth cultures for as long as we are able to track the history of medicine. How can we use it now to instruct us on how to move through life/death cycles to restore health on spiritual, emotional, and physical levels? How can we apply our own forms of Alternative and Complementary Medicines in the current context of modern medicine to form more balanced structures for healing illness and disease in ourselves, in our families, in our communities, and on the globe?

Come, step inside, let me tell you a story.

CHAPTER TWO

El Gallo Macho y la Reina de la Cocina

The Macho Rooster and the Queen of the Kitchen

The Northern Shield

Adulthood

WINTER

Winter is cold and internal. If we listen and allow ourselves to drop into what is really being reflected outside, there is the possibility for deep reset and nourishment. We are being asked to let go completely into a symbolic death. Following this impulse, we have the opportunity to align with something so deep and rich, and then come out the other end feeling quiet, restored, and well—as long as the death and the dying are complete.

THE ELEMENTS AS TEACHERS

The lessons of the seasons can be described in the essential teachings of each element: water, air, fire, and earth. (While some traditions acknowledge five elements in their relational health theories, we are working here with four, as the Medicine Wheel instructs.) Each one embodies a nature that reflects an aspect of our human nature, and the phases we move through as we cycle through our lives, in both macrocosmic and microcosmic motions. We'll start in the North. Here, in the symbolic space of an adult, we assume responsibility for what we create.

WATER

The lessons of water are the embodied teachings of relationship. Relationship, heightened by polarity and the natural attraction of opposites, sits at the heart of our truest bliss and our deepest sorrows.

Water is the element of feeling. Symbolically speaking, it is where our emotions live. The lessons water offers are connected to our deepest experiences of feeling. When our feelings are dark, they include loss, betrayal, and power. The dark lessons in winter teach us the lived experience of death—the truest polarity to life—and the ecstasy possible within it. Water, the element that holds things together and births new life, also shows us the danger in holding too tight or for too long. We must learn, like water, to be fluid, receptive, and patient. Just like how we must learn to be in our relationships—to self, to other, and to the places where we walk.

My soul speaks in Spanish. It's where my laughter lives. And my heartbreak. And everything in between. Here, in Spanish, there is an inherent understanding that to have Love, you must have separation. Polarity. Distinction. So even the words are kept separate. Some are masculine. Some are feminine. It's a language laced with longing and filled with space. It's a place where life can constantly emerge, then fold back in on itself. It's a language not about getting somewhere, but about *being* somewhere, alive on this ever-fruiting earth.

Sometimes, this feels like a real reverence for the feminine. The masculine takes care of the feminine by making her "La Reina de la cama," "La Reina de la casa," or "La Reina de la cocina." It is richly territoried, and the house belongs to her. I like this. Until I realize that, while the woman belongs to her house, the man may belong to many houses. Seeding and fruiting where he pleases. This reverence that the man has for a woman too often leaves him wanting more. Some women can live with this. I am left feeling forever unsafe.

Sometimes, when I lose my way, I refer to an ancient book of wisdom and divination called the *I Ching*. At first, it seems like a parlor game: ask a question and get an answer. Cool. The answers are rich and diverse enough and always seem to respond to my question, as long as my questions are crystal clear. Of course, the responses in the book leave room for interpretation. So you can take them or leave them, depending on your humor.

But my humor now is dark and doubting. Afraid. And alone. My house is armed with alarms, both internal and external, along the thresholds of all of the doors and windows. Every time a door opens, I hear a beep. Just to remind me I am not safe—to heighten my vigilance and keep me aware.

The *I Ching* will tell me this is simply one state of relational being. There are many. Sixty-four relational states of being, to be exact. They could also be called frameworks. This suggestion alone is enough to comfort a woman who was raised being told to "smile," "be nice," "don't be so sensitive," "be gentle," "lower your voice." When you're asked to always be in harmony, it seems such a relief to hear that disharmonious states are just as real and relevant as their less agreeable neighbors.

So I feed often from *I Ching*. Over the course of many years I've been delighted to discover the Four hexagrams that even speak directly to our nourishment. One of each is included here as we explore the seasons, for you to taste the multiple possibilities for your own nourishment.

Let's start with this one:

I Ching #48 Well

Well is the symbol of Source. Nourishment. Refreshment. In ancient times The Well was the heart of the village and the community. The place where women went to draw up a bucket from the deep, stone-walled throat of a tunnel that touched down into the clear, clean pool of unadulterated water. The water, drawn up to quench the thirst of an individual and a family, also symbolizes the resources needed to feed and sustain the crops and thereby the entire community.

The Well, a meeting place, source of communion and of refreshment, also alludes to one's inner nature. One must be careful to attend to its maintenance and structure and to not drink from a polluted well. The physical structure is supported as long as The Well is maintained.

RELATIONSHIPS IN HEALTH AND HEALING

Relationship is a biological imperative, wired into us to ensure survival. The depth, intimacy, and functionality of what we live in relationship—to ourselves, to others, and to the landscapes and elements in which we live—impacts our health on every level, from spiritual to psychological, from emotional to physical. How we feel inside our most intimate or important relationships plays a pivotal role in all aspects of our health.

Jean Achterberg, PhD, said, in the closing Plenary session at the Annual Symposium, Creating Integrative Health Care, San Diego, CA 1998, "That relationships are healing is no longer in question from a research perspective." Research on the impact of relationships—on our hormone levels or endocrine systems, on how they impact gene expression and DNA repair to thus influence immunity and the disease process, on how healthy relationships biologically impact parenting and reproductive behavior—has been thorough and conclusive. The influence of relationships on the shape and health of our nervous systems, endocrine systems, and immune systems is evidenced through well-designed, scientifically controlled experiments that explain our biological responses to relational bonds and the feelings they create.[1]

In Achterberg's words, "Ordinarily, we would drop everything to study and facilitate any medicine that has proven this robust. This enduring. This ubiquitous. This is not about medical treatment, not about psychotherapy. It is rather, about the most basic, primal, exalted events of our lives— our relationships."[2]

Still, this topic lives on the fringe of accepted science or fact. It is considered private, personal, and as something to be explored in self-help or psychotherapy. Yet medical doctors remain riddled with increasing incidents in infertility, diabetes, compromised immunity, and stress-related disease. Digestive disorders and complications are also on the rise and met with a dearth of support and understanding within the medical community.

If we can start with the acknowledgement that relationships do indeed play a key role in both our emotional health and our biological health—influencing entire systems from the immune, to the endocrine, to the nervous, to the digestive systems—then we have a new starting point to work with, a new frontier for encountering the entire spectrum of health, from self-care to medicine.

Then, we must also consider not just our relationships to other human beings or loved ones, but to ourselves and to the places we inhabit. How one thinks of him/herself, and the dialogue he/she perpetuates in his/her own mind, is primary. Other relationships fall into place around that.

The first time I fell in love, I mean with the man I would come to marry, it was safe. He was older, so mature, so kind and thoughtful. I still laugh when people tell me how kind and thoughtful my children are, and I reply, "We thank their father for that!"

Me? I am not kind. Well, "nice" is the word I use. But I am not nice. I am real. I am sincere. I am honest. Please, don't call me nice. At least that is what I used to say.

So I married this man. And he was safe. Safe in the way that he really listened when I spoke, and he stepped back when I had big feelings, not asking me to put them away or to change them. He just made space for them and let them be. Safe because he really loved all of me, and he was fully committed to that love.

"I will never compromise our relationship for power, or trade in this (our loving ways) for a power struggle. I've seen it happen too many times. I will not do it," he told me. And it was true.

So I learned a new way of relating. A new form of intimacy. It was kind and gentle. It was expansive and supportive. He liked to work. I liked to cook. He was trained as a classical chef in reputable French restaurants and kitchens. Though he was now committed to brand strategy and developing small companies, he was available day and night for my inquiries on food alchemy. I got to spend endless hours in the kitchen, playing with living ingredients and seeing how they interact and complement each other. He got to go to work. Then, I got to feed him. This, for me, is an act of love unto itself. Within it, I am complete. Especially when the eater loves to eat. So we found a balance in the simple ways that we cared for each other and for ourselves.

It was a huge success, for 10 years, until I realized it was always "nice." Where was the friction? The disagreement? The factors for dynamic growth and expansion? Is this all there was to it? Me here, all of the time, years later with two little boys. Him out, all of the time with new team members at fabulous restaurants in endless cities.

Where is he?

Had I married my mother? The one I adored so much who was never there? Or so it seemed to me.

The man who had scooped me up and fed me in ways I had never even imagined, who had come to re-program my entire relationship to food and nourishment, would now have to let me go.

Bitter Tea - *in the winter, when lemons are in season, I send my boys to fetch them from trees throughout our neighborhood. It is a task that delights them and brings me one of the most essential ingredients in the kitchen, a lemon. I have even started to travel with a lemon, like a toothbrush, as part of my kit. Once in Portugal when I was a girl, we had lunch on a large finca with a big lemon orchard. I will never forget having tea after lunch, as a digestive to help move the large meal. It was made simply from water and the rind of a bitter lemon. Plus, the fragrance of any citrus fruit truly does lift one's spirit.*

Rind from a lemon - washed and preferably organic
Peel and use at least 1/2 the rind per cup of water
1 to 2 cups water
Humor
Sugar or Honey to taste - optional

Place water to boil over medium heat on stove. Add lemon rind. Boil for 5 to 7 minutes on low boil. Remove from heat and let sit some 10 minutes to cool, which will concentrate the medicinal properties of the rind. Serve as a tea, sweetened or not.

BOUNDARIES AND ENERGETIC SAFETY

How do we set boundaries when it's time to go?

Setting boundaries and saying no have perplexed me since adolescence, when my own "Nos" were confused with the "Nos" that my mother, father, and community put in place. No wonder saying "No" to a man and holding lines with my children have been so taxing. It's not something I learned as part of the adult feminine way.

But saying no—not just an instinctual or reactive no we put in place at the last minute for survival and safety, but a gentle, clear no before we reach our limit—is a foundational part of how we maintain our health and support our well-being.

So, when my seven-year-old is asking for food "NOW" as in "IMMEDIATELY," or my adolescent is swearing at me when I am not able to respond right away or in a way that he likes, then my ability to draw lines and set expectations with them is foundational to supporting myself. "Why is it…" I finally ask my mama friend, the one who is so sturdy and unapologetic with her "Nos," the one who has two young children, but still shows up for work and for her friends with nothing short of aplomb, presence, and kindness, "Why is it that when their dads tell them "no" and set a boundary, they listen with no retort? And with me, they are constantly challenging and crossing the lines!?"

"It's like that for me, too!" Alice insists. "They just listen to Brian. Could it be a male/female thing?" She suggests in her easy, accepting way. There's the tone of the man's voice versus the woman's. There's the fact that this child once lived inside of the woman, feeding from the placenta and blood that she supplies. The embryo that will be the child is completely integrated and one with every sound, feeling, gesture, thought, and experience she has. When expelled from the bliss of total fluid warmth and unity, the baby finds itself outside of the mother, it then suckles her breast and, in my case, shares her bed for at least three years. Could that have something to do with why setting boundaries with my own children is so hard?

I see often how my own sense of boundaries is more deeply intertwined with my ideas about love, what love is, what love looks like, how it is lived in the discreet portraits and larger landscapes that shape the experiences, and then the memories of my life. I have watched it ruin my intimate relationships, as I confuse love with being available when I am really not, or would prefer not to be.

In Craniosacral therapy, and the embryological theory that informs cranial work, we believe that the blueprint for our intimate relationships begins before birth.[3] It is ignited at conception with the energetic bond between mother and father, and will be influenced by the climate they are in when the child is conceived. It is further influenced by the parents' energetic memories and the patterns laid out in ancestral relationships, experiences, and lived traumas that would have impacted the imprint of health, both psychological and biological, in those people.[4] [5] Research is still catching up with this concept, the idea that we carry our ancestors' experiences in our blood, and it is a ripe area of interest and inquiry in the field of Evolutionary Psychology, which claims that indeed, "survival strategies are passed along in our DNA."[6]

Equally important, one's sense of love and intimacy is set up by the child's relationship to mother and their shared experience before, during, and the two years following birth. After birth, the role of the primary care giver becomes paramount. The depth and quality of contact between mother/primary care giver and child during this period sets the initial blueprint for intimate relationship in her child's life. It is the groundwork that the child has to refer to as he/she finds his/her way from the mother (caregiver), into other intimate relationships later in life.

The level of intimacy and safety established initially between mother and child depends on the mother's sense of safety in the world and how her nervous system is organized at that tender time.[7] The health of her nervous system depends firstly on what she lived as a baby (before, during, and after birth) within her family dynamic. Secondarily, it depends on the personal work she has done as a conscious young adult/adult to restore equilibrium and freedom to her nervous system and the contingent biological systems. This restorative work then will inform what she is living within the current context of her family life with partner.

These are the patterns we observe in embryological and cranial studies to understand just how lived experiences map themselves into our bodies and how patterns transfer through generations along family lines. Our ideas about boundaries, what is safe, and what is appropriate or not gets set up in these early years. In addition to all of the ideas we inherit from our parents around how to behave, what to say or not to say, how to approach or stay away from others, there is an energetic transmission that occurs. Our energetic maps and their health and vibrancy are, like roads and highways, being laid out and constructed here in these tender times.

How does your mother respond to people, people she knows, and those she doesn't know? Is there a discrepancy between what she says and the feeling quality you (the child) experience and she experiences, as she says it? As she interacts with others?

What about your father? How is he in relationship to others? Does he interact with ease and trust or doubt, distrust, and fear? Is there alignment between what he truly feels when he speaks or interacts and what he says? What is your felt sense of the situation?

The information you pick up as you observe and feel your parents is foundational in how you shape your experience of trust, safety, and boundaries in the world. First with your parents, and then with your mentors and in your relationships outside of your home. It is not something cognitive or learned later in conversations or educational settings. It is a felt sense being wired into you, into your visceral experience, as you grow.[8]

BOUNDARIES AND MEDICINE

Your ability to trust and interact in a field of safety and self-assurance then informs how you will create boundaries, particularly when you step out of the protective shield of your family, typically at age 13.[9] In Chinese Medicine, we see these energetic boundaries as a protective shield that literally forms your primary defense or immune system throughout your life. It is an energetic shield called Wei Qi which extends out from your core organs (the kidneys, the spleen, the lungs, and the heart) and into the field around you. It is a critical piece of protection, both on an energetic level and then a physical level.[10] Unlike modern medicine where immunity is perceived as a biological system with its headquarters in your thymus gland and its protection the white blood cells that act like soldiers who attack and consume viruses, bacteria, and germs, the Wei Qi is a protective shield that stops the threat of wind, cold, damp, and the things that make you ill *before* they "hit" the body.

This form of thinking extends across disciplines through Qigong, to Polarity therapy, through centuries-old practices of Shamanism into current explorations of field theory. The idea is that there is a field of energy that emanates from you, and when it is strong, it protects you from illness before the illness reaches your body.[11] It is influenced by how you occupy your own space, by experiences in your early years, by diet, what you eat and drink, by your thoughts (if they are positive, optimistic, trusting, and life-affirming, or not), by the openness and resilience of your heart, and by the everyday activity that re-enforces and strengthens your musculoskeletal system. Many of these are unconscious and subconscious qualities. Regardless, your field of protection is impacted by where you put your boundaries, your ability to discern where to says YES! and where to say NO!

Health (and immunity) is therefore in your hands and is deeply influenced by your early life experiences, your lifestyle, and finally your alignment with who you are. This alignment, hard-earned for most of us, is what makes your heart sing and your health thrive.

At ages 12 and 13, I learned to speak Spanish. Not just Castillan Spanish from Spain, but also Argentine Spanish from Argentina, and Mexican Spanish from Mexico, and Central American Spanish from Nicaragua. Of course language is only a portal into another universe. It teaches us to construct reality in different ways and offers us, in words and how they are put together or left out completely, different ways of experiencing not just each other and place, but also ourselves.

But it's not only the Spanish language that seduces me. It's also the music and the food. The roots in the country of Spain are deep and complex. There are many layers, lending both to dark and light. At least this is what I felt as a little girl the first time I saw Flamenco.

The dancers on the stage were unlike any women I had seen before. They were not aspiring to "look nice," to "be agreeable," or even "be modest." They were dark and richly adorned and were there to showcase their pain. The extreme showiness of their layered and ribboned dresses was only a balance, a polarity, for the mysterious and stern looks on their faces. When they danced, they danced by pounding their feet. And when they extended their arms and folded their hands inward and outward it was not just movement in their bodies, it was the expression of an entire life story. Their arms, hands, fingers spoke the feelings of their hearts. And the feelings there looked, to my 12-year-old eyes, hard and dark and painful.

Everything about Flamenco, the women, the music, and the motion was mature and unfamiliar. When the women sang, they moaned, voices deep, even masculine. And when the men played guitar, it was in response to what they saw in the women in front of them. This level of intimacy and connection between musician and dancer awakened something in me that had only been sleeping before. It let me imagine that perhaps there really was a landscape for all that I felt inside as well as various instruments to call this inner self forth. So I learned to speak, to eat, to dance, and to see in all of these Spanish ways. For me, Spanish culture was an essential portal into adulthood, and the rich complexity I felt adulthood was meant to embody.

"You must remember that a teaching that is true, is always true, in any culture with any language attached to it." —**The Book of Mastery**

Dinner in Spain is light and festive. It embodies the late night energy of winding down and honors the idea that you will be resting, not digesting, soon, so it makes sense not to eat as much.

Sopa del Jardin (Gazpacho) - *a simple way to use fresh, raw vegetables as well as day-old bread. The raw garlic gives it flavor and life, and it helps to boost the immune system and fight infection. Tomatoes are high in vitamin C and trace minerals. Cucumbers cool the body and nourish the skin. Olive oil, perfectly balanced in omega fats, is an ideal fat to include in any meal. Fats are an absolute essential in the diet to maintain nerve health and ultimately endocrine and immune function. The right kinds of fat not only create healthy skin, hair, and nails, they keep your deepest organs functioning at ideal capacity.*

3 to 4 ripe tomatoes
1 chunk of day-old baguette (no bread or gluten-free bread are options!)
2 cloves garlic
1 cucumber
1 wedge of onion
Approx. 4 cups water
1/4 cup olive oil
Desire
Salt to taste

Combine in blender and blend until smooth and creamy. Salt to taste. Dress up with sour cream (or avocado for dairy-free addition), chopped cucumbers, extra chopped onion... whatever your pleasure.

I gave up languages when I came to Cachiquel, an Indigenous language spoken in the Western Highlands of Guatemala, halfway between Guatemala City and Quetzaltenango. I was there, in a town called San Jose Poaquil, not to learn the language of the people, but of the plants. I was there to study with a Mayan Medicine woman who could teach me how to seed, care for, harvest, and transform local plants into medicine. The thing is, the local people no longer employed these plants as medicine. Many of the plants grew as weeds in their gardens: mint, apazote (wormwood), yarrow, hibiscus, and others were cast aside and trampled as one gathered his/her monthly savings to run down to the general store for a pharmaceutical solution. My volunteer work in the garden seemed irrelevant compared to the desperate need to preserve this information and transmit it back to the local people.

But four months into it, only just then being invited to bathe with my local family in their tuj (mud bath) after months of cold showers in afternoon sun, I gave up. Not just because the

Cachiquel people had already given up on their local plant remedies, and there was in-fighting in the garden/children's center where I worked, and a flea in my sleeping bag for two weeks, and our plant offerings became a trendy boutique souvenir at the local health food store in Antigua, but because I couldn't speak their language.

We were sitting together one night at the dinner table in our semi-outdoor kitchen, which was dimly lit with the embers of a true wood-burning stove. Antonietta sacrificed the duck she cared so well for during the past months, to roast in her adobe oven. Evelyn, her five-year-old daughter, pulled handfuls of corn from the bucket that they had taken earlier to the mill to grind, and patted them into tortillas to eat with the duck. But the lighthearted smiles usually on their faces were turned down.

"What is it?" I ask them in Spanish. Since I do not speak their native tongue Cachiquel, we meet in the middle.

There are four generations here in this home. The great-grandmother, who speaks only Cachiquel. The grandmother, my teacher in the garden, who speaks Cachiquel and some Spanish. Her son and daughter-in-law, Samuel and Antonietta, who are fluent in Cachiquel, but more so in Spanish. And Evelyn, the child who will come to speak mostly Spanish and English. Samuel's sister, Irma, still weaves her clothes by hand on a traditional loom and is teaching Evelyn to do so. Here, in 1998, they still make huipil shirts of colorful thread, row by row on a backstrap loom. The women dress daily in their traditional attire, a huipil with a denim color skirt.

"Oh, just a story about a woman who helps with the children at the center, Ri Palamax," where we tend the garden, Antonietta translates for me.

"Yes, what is it? What happened?" I insist.

"Her husband beat her." She tells me, her eyes cast to the ground.

"Beat her? Why?"

"Well, you see," she says, with reluctance. There is something she doesn't want to tell me, but she starts to smile and continues on, "Her husband says you are a boy. Or young man."

"Yes?" I ask, still not understanding what is going on.

"Well, because you work the way that you do in the garden, in boys' clothes (my corduroy pants and sneakers), he insists you are a man."

"And?"

"And he thinks his wife had relations with you."

"What?" I burst out. Laughing. Then they also start to laugh, as they do, so easily, with everything.

"Her husband beat her for having 'relations' with me!?" The family, seated peacefully on their hand-woven chairs on the mud floor of the kitchen, which is a corrugated tin roof and woven palm walls, is smiling. My smile fades as the story sinks in.

These are the pieces that do not translate: A young western woman coming to offer a hand in a local garden project is wise enough to do what is asked of her with the plants, so that she may learn the language of their Indigenous medicine. But she does not, cannot, will not ever understand the mind of the Indigenous man in the 21st century, and the danger she causes his wife by simply being there, in her pants, which to them makes me look like a young man, with her shovel and notebook.

So the danger and the irony are written on the wall some 20 years later when I, a Western woman, choose to have my children with a man from a traditional culture.

 Fill My Belly Vanilla Cinnamon Cacao (Atole)- *Atole, like milk or a thin oatmeal, was a typical breakfast or afternoon snack for us when I lived with the Indigenous Mayans in Poaquil, Guatemala, 25 years ago. Warm, semi-thick, sweet, and nourishing, Atole can take the place of hot milk with honey, hot cocoa, and even coffee. It offers a solution in the current climate of controversy around cow's milk, allergies to soy or nut milks, and packaging waste with cartons. It can even solve the problem when there is "nothing" in the house to eat. In Poaquil, it was made of fine grain corn flour, but I have found that mixed legume flours like garbanzo, fava, and mesquite offer a wonderful alternative with a different nutritional profile. It restores fluids to a mother who has just given birth and is agreeable to her newborn's digestive sensitivity.*

1/2 cup fine grain corn flour, blue or yellow, or play with folding in other grain flours
4 cups water
2 to 4 tbsp honey or syrup to taste
A pinch of salt
Pieces of cinnamon
Compassion
(Option to add milk or cacao to taste. Anise seed can also be a wonderful addition.)

Combine flour and water and cinnamon or other spices in a heavy saucepan over medium heat on your stove. Whisk vigorously over low to medium heat for 12 minutes or so, until frothy and slightly thickened. Add pinch of salt and honey or syrup to taste.

CONSTRUCTING A NARRATIVE

Just as important as the experiences we live are our memories of those experiences. The story or narrative we construct around a lived experience imprints itself on the body and comes to shape our realities even more than the experience itself. Stanley Krippner, a pioneer in the field of transpersonal psychology, describes these personal narratives as myths.

The word "myth" is used to fully communicate the amplitude that our personal stories hold—from spiritual to psychological and from emotional to physical. Our experiences and memories translate into us and through us to imprint as archetypal, soul stories. We often remain unconscious of how these myths shape our lives and how they direct or rule us, but introspective work and observation can uncover these personal myths and give us the choice to replace them or not. The "Myths can be adaptive or maladaptive to facilitate reality or retard growth."[12] How we see ourselves will ultimately influence our health, so becoming conscious of our archetypal stories is a profound tool for transformation. We can imagine these stories are like atoms which can shift from particle to wave, from a discreet object to a shifting fluid one. Changing the story and how we hold a memory can have implications on our quantum health.

So I continue with a new narrative, bowing into the story until I can start to see it for the flowering garden that it is.

"Sometimes people need a story, more than food, to stay alive." —**Indigenous Elder**

Twenty years later…

"Como son los hombres Latinos?" I repeated the question the man sitting across from me asked. What are Latin men like? "Los hombres Latinos son muy atrevidos," I replied, without hesitation. He burst into big bold laughter, as amused and delighted by this reply as I was. Yes. Latin men are bold.

We were sitting, just the two of us, at a table for four beside the painted turquoise wall across from what an American girl might describe as a diner bar. It is one of the restaurants in the Mission where they serve his native Nicaraguan Cuisine.

"Que vamos a comer?" He continues, still beaming. Beaming in a solid, masculine way I find so strong and irresistible.

"A ver… Compartimos un pescado?" Want to share a fish? I asked him.

"Hmmmm. No creo. Tal vez pido una carne." He said he'll have a steak.

When the waitress arrived, we ordered two Tonya's, Nicaragua's beer, a steak, a fish, a salad, and Gallo Pinto, which is rice and beans Nicaraguan style. They are folded together and fried in oil until dry and salty.

"Asi que aqui estoy con la Olivia." (Olivia is my first given name.) So here I am with Olivia he marvels, still in awe of his good luck. My heart is warm, marveling at my own.

There's a simplicity in this. The restaurant. The innocence of the tacky blue-green color on the wall. The lack of presentation of the bar/counter. Even the light fixtures are unselfconscious, there only to light the room, nothing more. Everything is what it is. Functional. Tasty. Real.

The food is made for nourishment and for feeding. So the fish comes with bones, and the steak is probably two and a half pounds. It fills the giant oval plate. He eats all of it, knowing hunger well and how to eat when it is time to eat.

One of my favorite rituals we had come to have around food is not talking while we eat. "Comer es para comer," he said, after his mother. So, stop talking and eat your food. This concept is the opposite of what I was told or shown in my lifelong education of the art of social grace and how to make clever conversation with dinner partners. I am relieved when I can just eat and breathe. "Just notice the food in your mouth," I say to my children now when they are talking and distracted while eating. "Imagine everything that happened in order to get that food onto your plate. From the planting of the seed, to the growing it. Then harvesting, transporting, acquiring, and preparing. The amount of breaths, gestures, resources, and people that go into getting those ingredients onto your plate are infinite. So please, at least notice it. Pay attention. Give thanks. And I don't mean thanks to me."

He's stuffed after the steak and showed me the possibility of loving that feeling: being stuffed with food. I tend to prefer the other one, emptiness. But the full quality of contact here was just right. We took each other's hands as we walked out the door.

His boldness, my delight. His masculinity, my womanhood. This is the polarity that births families. So, we had a child.

He brought me a harvest of beets and carrots from his garden in Oregon where he was working. And on Saturday, when he would come to visit, we would spend the day shelling beans from his harvest, or plucking feathers from a chicken he had raised. Then there was the time he brought me those dried seeds from the tree of a bitter orange. His son had sent them from Nicaragua. Bitter Orange!? Brilliant. He must be my true love. I am the queen who would not eat breakfast until one day they brought her marmalade.

It was a form of Abundance that any Literature major with a minor in Latin American Studies who once lived in Central America would give her heart and both arms and legs for. So, I did.

When the second child came and the conversation shifted from, "What shall we eat?" to, "How, exactly, are things going to work in this home, with all these moving parts?" including my children from another father moving in and out, and his other children across the bay. Including our views on how life works, mine as a modern American woman living in California, and his as a traditional Central American man whose first language is Spanish and second, masculinity. It was then things got more complicated.

I felt safe, yes, the night I gave birth to Alexei into his hands. It was Christmas, and we had spent the entire day at home, together with Remi, our older son. He watched a movie while I weathered my contractions and repeated to myself, "I am opening. I am opening."

"Come on, open your eyes. You're missing the whole movie," he intimated as he nudged me and pointed at the screen. I just smiled. And breathed.

Yes, this is what I had wanted. Even with him focused on the movie, this was it. Intimate. Connected. Quiet. Simple. A continuation of life inside of the intensity and death of birth. My desire was based on a movie I had seen about a woman giving birth in a Central American country. The movie showed her at the lunch table with 15 to 20 of her closest relatives even while she was in active labor. There she was, eating with them, while she made her way through the most dramatic of rites of passage. She was not separate or removed from her home and garden and placed in a hospital or birthing unit. She was there, giving birth at home inside of the wild and diverse garden of her family landscape. So, even in my less wild and diverse landscape, inside my home in Marin County in the winter, with my man and our older son watching a movie, I was pleased.

It was 8 pm and dark when I went outside to walk. The contractions were harder now and consuming all of my ability to manage pain. I sent a note not to my midwife, but to a craniosacral friend who had supported me through other births in her gentle and understanding way, just with her words.

"No words now. Just surrender," she wrote. "Breathe. Let go into it."

I walked with these ideas and my breath to the edge of the neighbor's fence. Then I heard a voice, "Olivia, Olivia." Yes, I am not safe here all alone, now, I thought. The baby is coming. I made my way back to the house.

"Did you call to me?" I asked him when I came in.

"No," he replied.

"It's too much now, I need support," I said. He didn't understand, but called the midwife anyway. She would come now.

Then he took one hand and had our three-year-old take the other. We moved, because you couldn't call it walking, slowly in a path that circles the rooms of the house.

"If you need to push, then push," he said to me in Spanish. "I got you."

Yes, he had me. I knew this was true.

Just a moment later I started to push. I had done the work to open and the path was as clear as I would get it. "There's a sheet on the bed," I said, responding to his concern about making a big mess. It's ready for us.

We lay me down on my side. I could feel the burning sensation I remembered of when the head is about to emerge. So I got behind it. And, in an act of sheer will and the perfect combination of power and surrender, I pushed. Alexei came out, in his sac, into his father's hands. It was 10:10 pm. The midwife would arrive 35 minutes later.

"Everything is good," she reassured us. "You did an amazing job," she said to him and to me. "How did you know how to do that?" she asked.

"Oh you know, I grew up on a farm. I saw lots of baby calves being born," he replied.

He managed it with perfect aplomb. There wasn't a moment I wondered if we were safe or ok. He was composed and present when he ushered me from the bathroom to the bed, when he held me, and when he laid me down on my side. He was confident in the way he stood, waiting for the baby to present itself, reassuring his three-year-old that everything was ok.

The midwife cut the umbilical cord and tied it off. She gave me goldenseal to treat the umbilical wound in the next couple of weeks. She weighed that baby and made sure all of his vitals were good. When the activity was over and his dad was fast asleep in the front room, I offered her something to eat.

"Quieres comer algo?" Her native country is Peru. Her mother tongue is Spanish.

"Si, por favor," she accepts. "Si no es mucha molestia." If it's not too much trouble.

"Tengo tamales que me regalaron. Estilo Guatemalteco hecho de arroz y pollo envuelto en hoja de banano." Guatemalan style tamales made with rice and chicken, wrapped in a banana leaf, I told her.

"Wonderful!" she said.

So there I was, baby one hour old, serving the midwife tamales in my dimly lit kitchen in the late hours of Christmas night, while dad and his sons slept. I wondered how in the world my midwife had said "yes!" These are the true births of a mother, what I will later come to know as "sacred tasks," the impossible tasks we perform after hours of unsung heroic deeds, the ones we never knew ourselves capable of.

 **Vegetarian Papoose (Tamales)** - *not to be confused with Honduran Papusas, these wonderful corn-husk-wrapped treats truly add an ecological solution to a small snack or family meal. There is no need for a plate or utensils, and the husks go into the green bin when you are finished. They can be made ahead of time, and the process or experience of making tamales is as delicious and sensuous as eating them. Making tamales is also an excellent way to get your children in the kitchen and their hands in some "clean dirt." Then, they are earthy, grounding, balanced, and easy to freeze and pull out in a pinch for a nourishing snack.*

3 cups masa harina, available at your food store
2/3 stick butter (room temp.)
1 cup broth of choice
1 to 1 ½ cups water
1 pinch salt
1 pinch sugar (optional)
30 or so corn husks
1 to 2 cups black beans (recipe below)
Modesty
Salt to taste

Soak corn husks in flat glass 9 x 13 dish in boiling water for 30 minutes or until soft and supple.

Whip butter with a fork against a tall bowl. Leave on side and add masa. Pour broth into bowl while warm. When your or your children's hands are clean, combine ingredients with your fingers. "Batter" should be moist and stick together like playdough. Not dry or overly wet.

Nourish My Kidneys Black Beans - *Beans have been a staple in the Central American diet for centuries. Not only do they provide a source of amino acids and protein, they are also restorative for the deep energy we call "Jing" that helps replenish the kidneys' energy when, after months of running on adrenaline, it is used up. Then, there is the convenience of being able to store black beans on your shelf and pull them out at night to soak, so that you can prepare the next day to have as a meal and ingredient for days. In this recipe, I am assuming they are there and ready to use, cooked and prepared.*

> *Leftover black beans*
> *1/4 cup broth*
> *Serrano chile*
> *Ripe tomato*

Blend 1/3 of your cooked beans in a blender with a slice of Serrano Chile and 1/4 cup broth. Combine over stove with the remaining whole black beans, then add a dab of butter to taste and a squeeze of tomato.

Create a workspace where you can lay out 3 or so husks at a time. I use a large cutting board. Unfold husks and lay flat. Place just enough batter (approx. one tbsp) into center of husk and press down. Add a tsp of beans, and fold in sides and then the ends to create a little package.

Fill all the husks, laying each one face down, until you are done. Then, strip leftover husk into strips to use as ties, and tie off ends with either one or two strips, so package will remain closed.

Cook in strainer inside large pot with boiling water beneath for 30 minutes. Makes approximately 20 small tamales. Let cool, and freeze or serve.

"La casa sólo puede haber una cabeza," he said one day, months later… A house can only have one head.

Yes, in theory, I like the way he thinks. It is boundaried and clear. One's role is defined, and he/she can execute it with full commitment and clarity. This way of thinking, his way of being, has afforded me a femininity I never had before. It has ushered me into womanhood in a way that only this kind of polarized and dynamic partnership could. So, I did the dishes and mopped the floor, bathed the babies and fed them, washed the clothing and bedding, and got everyone off to school without wanting it any other way. This was while I was also carrying along a business making moccasins.

The expectation set the bar. Mothers have an infinite supply of love, time, energy, and willingness. That's what it's like where he comes from. I accepted this and rose to the occasion. Just shifting the way I thought gave me the strength, power, and perseverance to do it all. I became my own heroine, modeled after my true hero—the Latina Mama, the most generous, capable mothers on the planet. It is a status they have earned not with power, force, or glory, but with complete surrender and love. Available, present, willing, fierce, tireless, capable. They have no expectation of "taking space," or "time for themselves," he would tell me. They want to be with their babies all of the time. So I came to feel privileged in my continuous connection and commitment to it all.

Until things fell apart.

POWER

This idea, that we can take power out of the equation of a relationship is not true, in the end. POWER will always be at the center of an individual, a family, an organization, a relationship. To remove it is to take away the dynamics required for growth and evolution. Particularly in an intimate male/female partnership. How we balance our power within ourselves, and with each other, is foundational.

Understanding, yes, understanding is medicine for conflicts in power. Many nights I said to him, "I think perhaps there is a misunderstanding here." And I could, inside the energy of love, show him how I saw it. He listened with a storehouse of patience that amazed me over and over, though he often said nothing in response.

So we held "it" together. Until it fell apart.

I didn't feel safe anymore. And there was no way we could talk our way through it.

The first time I gave birth was not as graceful as the last time. I planned and practiced. Envisioned and breathed. Exercised and had eaten well. I received regular Acupuncture and Craniosacral treatments. I walked up Sacramento Street early every morning to practice Qigong at the labyrinth at Grace Cathedral. I even completed a course in "Hypnotic Birthing." But none of these came even close to preparing me for what it really was to bring a child from idea into seed, then fruit, and then finally birth into his own separate form.

No one had spoken to me about the true death required in birthing. It is not just the complete physical surrender that is so essential for a mother to pass a baby from its internal vault, down through her birthing canal, and into the external place it will now call home, but there is a psychological surrender as well. The arrival of a child marks the true end of the mother's childhood and the freedom and selfless expression that she hopefully knew there. Her independence, her creativity, her autonomy, and self-expression must all be put to rest as she too crosses a threshold from one state of being to another. Like the baby, who has just passed from its walled garden, out into a hungry and unshielded new reality, losing the union with both mother and source that are part of the embryological development, the mother passes from one state of being to the next. And, having lost not just her old identity, but the comfort of god-consciousness that was just growing in her belly, this new place can be cold and hard. It is no wonder we have a term for it: *postpartum depression.*

It was 1 am when I finally felt the contractions that would bring the baby through. There had been hints in the weeks before that had fooled me. But none were as focused and fierce as these. When I finally decided to face them, I got up out of bed and rolled onto a sheepskin in the windowsill. In the shadow and privacy of the darkness, I breathed and moved and prayed for mercy.

But my prayers were still only an idea. Hour after hour I chased the sensation of contraction, thinking there was something I could do or think to make the pain more bearable. A different position? A different way of breathing? A different thought? Was there something I could control to make it all better? The impossibility of it stayed, even as dawn broke and my husband came to join me in my process.

Finally, he called the Doula. "No, no, she's ok," I think I heard him say to her. We were told to count the contractions, so we did. Sort of. What was that again? I couldn't seem to track it.

"I can't do this anymore," I said to him. "I can't do it. Please, please can you call Linda?" Then Linda, the acupuncturist, was there, and at last I wrapped my arms around her shoulders, dropped my head onto her, and pleaded for help.

The help came in the simplest form: her understanding. Not because she had given birth, but with all of the births she attended and the expectant mothers she treated with her needles and the soft whisper of her voice, I felt like I could face it again. Or at least that I had an ally. She put me in the bath to warm my legs. And when I got out, I held my hips and put some needles into my sacrum. She helped me bridge the abyss between the slow sporadic contractions and the quicker closer ones. Then Rachel, the Doula, arrived to ferry us across the city to the hospital. It was now rush hour.

The baby was to be born at 5:42 pm on the second floor of St. Luke's Hospital in the Mission, where Yeshi Newman was allowed to have a program called homestyle midwifery, a true model of non-invasive midwifery care inside of a hospital facility. When I arrived and walked to the room, still convinced I couldn't do it anymore, it was Yeshi's gentle questions that, again, changed everything. "What is it?" she asked in the most authentic and curious way.

"I'm scared," I told her.

"Scared?" She paused, then continued. "Of what?"

She wasn't doubting that there were a million things to be afraid of. Just asking, what is it that was scaring *me* right then.

I didn't answer her, not out loud at least. The answer, "of the pain," was really only for me. Once I heard my own thought, I realized it couldn't get any worse than it had already been! All I could do now was "get out of the way," as we say in spiritual practice, and let whatever it was that really truly pushes this baby through have its way with me. I remembered Ina May's lesson from *Spiritual Midwifery:* You have the power to open and enlarge as much as the baby needs you to. Soften your mouth, open your lips, let yourself open. A moment later, Oliver's head emerged. Yeshi would say, "With his eyes, his intelligent eyes, wide open and curious."

Thank God the shoulders then came more easily, and the rest of him slipped out seamlessly. It was the greatest form of relief and surrender I would ever know.

But there was something else. It wasn't over yet. What was it? I knew Yeshi had to get to a concert with her daughter, but we were not done yet. "There's more to do? But what?" I said. Even with all of the birth preparation, I had no idea I had to birth the placenta, too!? But my body would not let it go.

Yeshi pulled very slightly. The team of nurses settled me onto the mattress on the ground and fed me my homemade breakfast bread. But my body would not let go of the placenta. Not until Yeshi whispered in my ear, "You are nourished. You have all you need already inside of you. You can let it go now." Ten minutes later the placenta finally came through.

After that, I think it was his smell I remember most. Dark and internal, alive and rotten, like the smell of fall. Fleshy, like inside the pork store in Tuscany. And clean, like spring water.

Another Doula came to collect the placenta to make medicine out of it, the way they've done in Indigenous cultures for centuries. She dried and ground it, then encapsulated it with ginger and cayenne. We were to take it to recover from birth, colds, flues, and even amnesia…the kind that comes when we forget to be in awe of everything. Only it was too spicy for him, my red head, and also for me, the over-heated, recently pregnant woman. So it sat in the freezer alongside the other frozen placenta I was to birth two years and 10 months later with Rafa.

Funny to see now, 13 years later, that Oliver seems to be my child who tries to think his way through everything. How much of how I gave birth is a reflection of this child's consciousness, I wonder?

 **Warm My Womb Applesauce Cinnamon Breakfast Bread** - *this delicious cake offers the comfort and sweetness of a good dessert, without all of the sugar or non-desirable fat. The cinnamon and nutmeg lend it a wintery feeling, while also improving its digestibility and immune-boosting capacities. The applesauce makes it moist, and the olive oil gives it a European twist that gets better as the days go by. And, for those who cannot see why cake would be in a book on "healthy" eating, I must say: cake for me, is an antidote for any woe. But physically speaking, the pre-digested ingredients of flour mixed with milk and oil is easy on a digestive system that has been on vacation. So it is a stepping stone back into the world of appetite and longing, where real health lives. If you choose gluten-free, simply substitute the wheat flour with 2 1/4 cups of gluten-free flour. I like to fold in other flours not only for texture, but because I find gluten-free flour to be high on the glycemic index, which means it gives a quick boost of sugar to the blood that I don't always prefer.*

1 ¼ cups gluten-free flour
1 cup whole wheat pastry flour
1 1/2 tsp baking powder
1/2 tsp baking soda
1/2 tsp salt

1 tsp ground cinnamon
1/2 tsp ground nutmeg
3 eggs, room temp
1/2 cup olive oil
1 cup unsweetened applesauce
1/2 cup milk of choice
1/2 cup maple syrup
Relief
1/4 cup molasses (optional - adds iron and depth/darkness to the cake)

Pre-heat oven to 350° and grease 9 x 3 glass baking dish with coconut oil (or other butter/non-stick of choice). Combine flours, baking powder, baking soda, salt, cinnamon, and nutmeg in a medium bowl, then sift through colander into another medium size bowl. In another larger bowl, whisk together the eggs, olive oil, applesauce, milk, syrup, and molasses until thoroughly combined. Fold the dry ingredients into the wet ones, and mix minimally. Pour into glass dish, and place in oven for approx. 40 to 45 minutes. When you smell the wintery scents of the cake baking is when it is almost ready to remove. Bake until firm all the way to the center of cake, which you can test with a knife, poking it into the center. When it comes out clean with no batter, it's ready to remove. Let cool and enjoy.

When Rafa came, I was way over the idea that there was something I could do to make birth better or more easeful. Now, after one birth and nearly three years of mothering, I was more tenderized to the truth of where my power actually begins, and where it ends. God, the Divine, softness, and surrender had a new place on my altar and in my awareness. The only real solution, or way through sleepless nights or inconsolable baby, was through surrender and softness. There was no willing my way through his digestive discomfort, and there was no way of doing it all "right." There was only listening, experimenting, testing, and watching. And the days that felt impossible and I was too tired to face it, it was the giving up and giving in that opened the way.

When Rafa came, the midwife, this time a German woman with fierce crystal blue eyes and an impenetrable strength in her jaw and mouth, said to me, "Yes, yes, you already have the food and body pieces. It's your mental hygiene we have to work with here. How will you manage the pain?" Then she told me the story of calling "Allah" into the air during the birth of her third (of five) children. The sound, what it meant, and how it felt when she spoke it, carried her through.

When I finally arrived at my answer, it was clear and simple. It would have to be physical though. I would have to "feel" God. So this is how I put it:

What does God feel like?

This is what I would say to myself when the contractions were too much to endure. This would be my focus, to feel into "God," not an idea of "him," "her," or "it," but a physical sensation. At least that's what I *thought* I would do.

In the end, even this thought or question wasn't strong or fierce enough to meet the sensation of what comes when a baby is working his/her way out of the female body and into the world. It is still philosophical, removed.

On New Year's Eve, when Rafa was coming and I snuck past the midwife, who was asleep on the couch, down into the privacy of a downstairs room, what finally came was much simpler still. It was:

I love you

Each time I felt a contraction during this birth, instead of resisting it, I said into it, "I love you." Everything I am feeling, the baby is feeling too. I am not alone in this. I am not alone, in this crisis of sensation, and remembering that, with the simple phrase, "I love you," carried us through.

He was born at 4 am on New Year's Day, also into his father's hands, out of a body that wasn't squatting or crouched as planned, but standing up and hanging off of the shoulders of the people there to support me.

Then, as the sun came up across the bay from Tiburon, we drank tea. Chamomile tea.

 Soothe My Sorrows Tea - *chamomile tea came to me through a Swedish mother, who used to give it to my siblings and me at bedtime to help us sleep as teenagers. It turns out that, not only is it a tonic for the nerves, it also soothes digestion and, when sweetened with miracle food like honey, helps one heal from birth…or so they say in Nicaragua.*

1 to 2 tsp chamomile flowers
1 to 2 cups water
Love
1 tsp honey (optional)

Place chamomile flowers in water over stove and bring to boil. Reduce heat and simmer 3 to 5 minutes. Remove from heat and let cool 15 to 20 minutes. Sweeten with honey if desired.

When Dara came to offer cranial support a couple of weeks after Rafa's birth, she came to support his digestion, his ability to latch on and feed, and to potentially correct any structural concerns the baby had after birth. These are typical concerns addressed post-partum with the gentle techniques of Craniosacral therapy. But her ample training as a baby whisperer provided one more piece that nobody had ever told me. Following our treatment she said to me, "Everything is good. So good. You clearly kept a connection with him throughout the entire birth."

There it was. A key that no mother, doula, book, midwife, or birth educator had ever mentioned to me. The goal in giving birth, more essential than any plan or pain management, was to KEEP THE CONNECTION WITH THE CHILD. To remember that this child was experiencing what I was experiencing, and to send it love, not resistance. Send love into every contraction. This was the magic of Rafa's birth, and yet again just preparation for the years that follow. I guess it shouldn't surprise me that Rafa is the one who always shows up in delight, playfulness, and love.

THRESHOLD MEDICINE - AT THE DOOR OF DEATH

Birth, an extreme exercise in learning to balance strength with surrender, is also a threshold where a woman comes face to face with her deepest form of power. But this only presents itself in the meeting, face to face, of the moment when you know you can't do it anymore. When you arrive at the portal of death, true death, your sense of your own power is gone. This moment, when in a hospital setting we are told is the time to reach for the support of a pharmaceutical solution, is the most critical. It is when you surrender into something bigger. The idea is that there is something bigger than you, your will, your capacity or training, your lessons or preparations, your husband or the doctor. It is when you meet God. Now God, a word so tainted by other people's ideas and lessons of who God is or what God means, here is offered as a word to describe that which holds you up when you can no longer hold yourself. God is the divine breath that moves through you, in inspiration and clarity, when your ego steps out of the way. In the moments of such extreme intensity, where death is no longer an idea or concept, but a neighbor at your door, is when we have the opportunity to meet our own definition of the divine.

Only in your willingness to believe in this possibility, and in your own courage to meet it, will you come to know that force. Birth, a real, literal threshold of death, is the true opportunity. And it is only preparation for what you need, in tools, to traverse the often fruitful, but sometimes barren, landscape of motherhood. It is here, when we come face to face with our greatest challenges, that we come to know who we really are. This potential, of deep intimacy with self, is the opportunity to claim who you are and the full health that unfolds from there.

BETRAYAL

In finding my way out of the heart of the labyrinth, the shadow side of my existence, I realized that I haven't felt safe in many things since I started to become aware of how things really are. There is fluoride in my drinking water and heavy metals in my toothpaste. There is factory pollution from products that I buy at the store in my air and in the water where we bathe. There are hormone disruptors in my teeth where my cavities were filled and in the bottles I use to drink water. There are harmful fats in the cookies I love from the store. I even pay money for them. The paint on the walls in my home has lead in it and can cause brain damage. I've spent 15 years recovering from wearing a back brace that doctors prescribed to correct a natural curve in my spine I had as a child.

The world is laced with land mines, and I am seeking out solutions that make me sick in the end. I am left over and over with a sense of betrayal.

Now, my voice is not even safe at home because, when I speak my truth, it causes conflict with my partner. That conflict wreaks havoc on my sense of boundaries and collapses my immune system. My skin is covered in rashes, and the food I eat then eats me, from the inside out.

Now what?

Any relationship that falls apart is devastating. And that means *all* of them, including parent/child, sibling, friendships, or partnerships. Especially when you rely so completely on each other for everything. Especially when there are children. Especially when there is conflict and no matter what happened, or didn't happen, a sense of betrayal.

The thing about betrayal is, it doesn't only happen between yourself and another. Betrayal happens when your trust is violated in any way. So we are betrayed by friends, by family, by partners, and by lovers as well as by institutions, organizations, companies, and systems. We are even betrayed by our own expectations and ideas about what "should be." Betrayal happens when something that we believed to be true turns out to not be true at all.

Betrayal is devastating and can wreak havoc on multiple systems, in our bodies, in our minds, in our communities, and beyond. When our perception of reality—what is solid, steady, and reliable—gets broken, the entire world as we have known it can collapse.

How do we even begin to put it back together again?

When we have chosen to put our trust into something external that no longer merits our trust and our devotion, how do we take back our lives and our power and move on?

What happens when things fall apart?

If we are lucky, we finally see what is broken and find ways to heal.

Only in our own willingness to look inside of ourselves do we find what we truly long for: what has been given away, and what now needs to be taken back. Reclaimed. Our medicine lives in the venom of the snakebite. It is the fire of our transformation. But it's up to us to see it and to make medicine out of it.

Is it possible to find my own way back to being well? Some days. The boys have to be fed, and I need to keep going. Food, and how we eat, is my territory. So I'll start here. What will nourish and feed seven generations? Seven is the number that marks the spiritual path, as it is only divisible by itself. In the number seven, one learns to stand alone, alone in partnership with the Divine. Seven generations was the standard native tribes set in making their decisions. *"How would their decisions in the NOW echo through seven generations of space and time,"* their leaders asked.

 **Nourish My Bones Broth** - *this lighter version of bone broth is nutritive and easy. You can add to sauces or use as the base of a soup in times of restoration. The essence of the bones in the broth is restorative and calming. It's easy on the digestive system and therefore ideal when one doesn't feel their familiar inner fire at work, as in times of stress, illness, low appetite, or poor digestion. It will nourish you and your family to the core.*

2 pounds of raw or roasted bones (beef, poultry, lamb, game)
Up to 1 gallon of water
1/2 to 1 onion, peeled
1 carrot
Inner leaves of celery heart

1 to 2 bay leaves
1 tbsp of vinegar (apple cider)
Intelligence

Place bones in a stock pot, and bring to a boil. Skim off the foam that comes to surface. Add the rest of the ingredients, and lower heat to simmer approx. 4 hours. Larger, denser bones can simmer up to 8 hours, smaller poultry bones up to 2 hours. Remove from heat, salt to taste. Once it's cool, you can pour into containers and place in fridge overnight. Then remove and skim off the extra layers of animal fat. Use in soups, drink for breakfast, or store in freezer for a later date. When serving, add salt and lime to taste. The lime gives it a fresh, live, and Latin America accent that distinguishes this broth from other versions.

THE SENSUAL EXPERIENCE: RECEPTIVITY AND FEMININE POWER

How we receive food, or NOURISHMENT, is how we receive LOVE.

The receptivity of the body is simple and consistent. It is an energy and a quality of being that allows you to take something in. It is the inhale in the cycle of your breath. And, while we are taught to believe that it is something automatic and mapped from the beginning into the autonomic nervous system, it is actually something that is altered through life experience and something we have the power to control.

Extreme life experiences, and chronic ones, impact our nervous systems and their ability to regulate our breath. With too much fast activity or visual stimulation, our breathing becomes short and accelerated. With shock, or trauma, our breathing can be interrupted and deregulated. In the case of too little stimulation, our breathing can be slow and tired. It is like a flaccid muscle that cannot support the weight of lived experience.

It is the same with our capacity to RECEIVE. Our ability to receive is altered by life experience. When we are overwhelmed, offended, betrayed, or disappointed over and over, our desire and capacity to take something in gets diminished. This impacts not only our emotional will, but our physical processing as well. The digestive system may slow down and lead to digestive problems and weight gain. Our creative sources may dry up or our ability to simply process stimuli may decrease.

Often, when we are hurt in some way, even what we eat cannot make us better. What I do know is that when I feel into that soft, receptive, loving place, everything about food, and about life, gets better.

So, like with a lover, I start with the sensual experience. My skin, my breath, my own gaze. I imagine letting love in and watch how my ability to eat food and receive nourishment shifts. Even just imagining "his" whisper in here is enough.

 **Sopa Vuelve a la vida: Come Back to Life Winter Green Soup** - *this soup offers aliveness in the dead of winter. Its flavors delight me. That feeling alone is enough to make me well. Then, there are the immune-boosting, anti-viral properties of garlic and greens. And the warming, anti-inflammatory aspects of Cayenne pepper. The soup is cleansing and versatile. It also has all of the flavors: salty, bitter, astringent, sweet, and pungent, which we say in Ayurveda makes a complete and satisfying meal. This soup has it all. Even a sense of "umami" from the olive oil, a round flavor that is associated with fat and offers great satisfaction in a dish. So no one is left wanting anything. The key is to pay attention.*

1 cup of 3 to 4 types of leafy greens, washed and patted dry (choose from watercress, parsley, arugula, cilantro, miners lettuce, frisee... simply what you like)
Approx. 4 cups water
1/3 green apple
1 date
1 and 1/2 tsps olive oil
1/4 to 1/2 lemon or lime juice
1/4 tsp salt or to taste
1 to 2 cloves garlic
Surrender
1/2 tsp cayenne pepper or to taste

Combine in blender. Blend until smooth. Refrigerate. Enjoy with a dollop of sour cream (or yogurt) and dose a of olive oil. Excellent with extra side of greens, sliced carrots, and feta or farmers cheese wrapped in a warm corn tortilla.

There are tools to restore the depth of receptivity that you deserve to embody. For me, the best one is visualization. When I remember the love I have lived and feel it all the way into my body, my body softens, and I feel energy drop down from my mind, toward my feet, and into the ground. I start to embody my idea of love here now. It's a union I can taste, massage, cultivate, and care for, even in the context of disappointment and failed expectations. And it helps me feel feminine again.

For me, this level of feeling and receptivity shifts how I show up...for my children, for my community, for myself. It allows a deeper level of perception and listening. This is a fuller presence, and, from here, I dance more playfully and attentive to what's showing up, now, to be addressed. It is an embodied form of adulthood that is able to engage both with children and with adults. It allows for both creativity and problem-solving. It also permits structure and fluidity within that structure. So adulthood, the essential teaching of the Northern shield, becomes whole, balanced in the polarity of both a masculine and feminine approach.

It is within this polarity that we discover the gift of the Northern shield and its role in how we assume responsibility to ourselves and to our communities.

Magnesium for deep winter sleep. One of the simplest, most innocuous remedies for sleeplessness is a Magnesium supplement. As a mineral and a coenzyme essential in the maintenance and regulation of the body, magnesium plays a vital role in balance of the endocrine system and is believed to help in nerve function, muscle contraction and relaxation, bone formation and maintenance, digestion and heart health.

God speaks to each of us as he makes us,

then walks with us silently out of the night.

These are the words we dimly hear:

You, sent out beyond your recall,

go to the limits of your longing.

Embody me.

Flare up like a flame

and make big shadows I can move in.

Let everything happen to you: beauty and terror.

Just keep going. No feeling is final.

Don't let yourself lose me.

Nearby is the country they call life.

You will know it by its seriousness.

Give me your hand.

Book of Hours, I 59 ~Rainer Maria Rilke

NOTES

CHAPTER THREE

En un Jardin de Cenizas

In a Garden of Ashes

The Eastern Shield

Elderhood

SPRING

Spring brings the promise of birth: new life, seeds that are ready to sprout. Our bodies, just like outside, start to thaw and speed up, eager in anticipation of the heat that is coming. What we eat needs to shift too—becoming not just lighter, but with a different quality of energy. It's less dense and more about energy. The difference between a seed, that is dense and packed with calories and nutrition, and a sprout, which is a seed that is open, rising, and more connected to the energy of fire and air.

THE ELEMENTS AS TEACHERS

When we turn clockwise to the East, we enter the elemental teachings of air. To be at home in the air element requires grace and a great surrender into what it is to be in wisdom of experience, as we see in our elders.

AIR

The lessons of air are the embodied teachings of Spirit and Connection. Air is the element of the mind and the ideas that move through it to inspire action. The mind, closely associated with the Spirit in Chinese Medicine, is the storehouse of illumination, transformative possibility, and pure potential. The lessons of air are interactive and fed again by our relationships—to ourselves, to others, to place, and to the Divine. With air, we see how our ideas penetrate others and vice versa, theirs penetrate ours. Here we begin to experience the great abundance of self-transformation and re-birth that is possible when we let others and their thoughts, their ideas, their cultures, and their beliefs interact with our own. In addition to the power of Spirit, the air element offers you the power of connection.

"Jump up and Live Again." —**Mayan Prayer from Martin Prechtel**

"Here, this is going to be my school," Alexei said, holding my hand and pointing to the little yellow house with the sign "Twin Cities Co-op" on the front. He said that every time we walked by. Perhaps because his brother was now in school. Perhaps because he remembered, and liked, the fall festival where he bobbed for apples from the school's apple tree, had his face painted, and made spin art just weeks before. Whatever the reason, he kept insisting, "Mama, here's my school."

So maybe it shouldn't have come as a surprise when they told me that there was a spot open for him. A school where, over the years I had inquired about sending my other children, there was a two-year waiting list. Plus, the requirements for attending "Twin Cities Co-op" seemed so rigorous: a workday with 25 children and four teachers once a week; a monthly evening business meeting; an ongoing chair position; helping with fundraising; setting up, attending, and breaking down the spring fling fund raiser; quarterly community events; plus a commitment to work on the property for basic maintenance four times a year. The monthly tuition, $330 for four mornings a week, was supposed to reflect the work trade. Ha! Welcome to California.

But I followed Alexei anyway, charmed by his conviction, and surrendered now to my own circumstances of being a single mom with limited income and an empty space where I had let my man replace my entire community. This, even beyond the failure of a relationship, was my biggest heartache. My greatest regret: having given up my entire community and best friends for a single relationship. I knew it then, and I know it still now, that a community—a strong, interconnected rainforest of essential life-giving relationships—is the best way to raise healthy children. So, we went for a tour of the school.

The tour, given by a mother, was perfectly professional. The admission process, headed up by a team of mothers, was seamless and easy. Aside from the vaccine requirement, for Alexei and myself, the path opened with no challenges. On January 7, my 44th birthday, Alexei began school at the Co-op.

The first stirrings of spring, I notice, come when the light begins to expand again—after winter solstice, the darkest day of the year. This is when I feel the first hint of thawing down deep, even if our surface climate takes time to catch up. And, with winter darkness now complete, we must begin a tale of spring.

I turn again to the wellspring of wisdom in the *I Ching* and rest inside of this hexagram on how we feed and nourish.

I Ching # 50 Cauldron

Cauldron is the symbol of nourishment. This time, it does not refer to the ordinary feeding of the people, but rather attention to the spiritual nature of man/woman. The symbol of Cauldron suggests the image of a cooking vessel hung over the burning logs of a fire. Here we see the union of man's basic need to feed his body, together with the essential requirement of tending to his spiritual self. The superior man knows this and compromises nothing for attention to his higher needs.

With Cauldron, we arrive in the Eastern shield, where the needs of the body not only give way to something more subtle, but… greater, perhaps? There is an ease that can happen when the needs of the physical vessel are met and the body is sustained. The spirit expands and one's needs for nourishment shift. Here we embody the light, and the folding of one's will into "God's" will is complete. Such is the essence of the Eastern shield of the Medicine Wheel and what it is to arrive in elderhood.

VISUALIZATION IN HEALTH AND HEALING

Visualization in the mind is a profound and transformational tool for healing. The power of imagery in healing can be traced back as far as we can go. The lens for seeing it changes, as images are the language of the soul, and how we perceive them and then communicate them depends on both cultural and personal influences. Imagery is the realm of the Shaman, but also the poet, the artist, and the mother. And so, images have been used to inform and transform the entire spectrum of human experience, as long as we have documented human life.

"Images, indeed all thoughts, are electrochemical events which are intricately woven into the fabric of the brain and the body." —Jeanne Achterberg

I find I often default to conversations and memories of "my lover," the man I have chosen to share my heart and my most intimate fears and longings. In my mind, I journey often to those places of shared intimacy and contact. These thoughts, sometimes memories and other times longings within themselves, are simple imaginations I have in time I spend with myself. They are part of my sanctuary for sorting out what I truly desire or am fed by. In short, these visualizations are my nourishment.

I call it my lover's voice. It surfaces and speaks to me when I need it the most. When reality is hard and unforgiving. The demands of being a mom alone at home with four young boys feels relentless and unrewarding. They are all talking to me at once, wanting to be witnessed or heard. Wanting to be fed, "IMMEDIATELY," or answered gently.

In truth, I know these conversations are at once the man I long for as well as my conversations with 'God.' As our ancient poets showed us, one's longing for love is equivalent to one's longing to be reunited with Source, as no man will ever meet a woman's full desire for union. Nor will a woman ever meet the man's idea of divine and complete love. Only 'God' can do this.

Woman to woman, man to man, man to woman—the relationships we live out are, again, this archetypal longing for union with Source. This knowing has been at the heart of original earth cultures and their rites of passage ceremonies since the beginning of tribal life. They knew and know that one must be *prepared* to live and love what is human, for this human will never live up to our expectations of "GOD"…of the Divine.

No wonder these visualizations are medicine that shifts my nervous system into a place of ease and connection. They bring me to a place where I can feel my body and savor my breath. With my imagination alone I have the power to shift my entire neuroanatomy.

"Would it be ok if I stayed with him, just until he is comfortable," I asked the director. "We had an experience at daycare where I left him for too long (4.5 hours), and he refused to go back," I said. I didn't tell her the parts about his dad leaving or how he left and just what my leaving might feel like after that, at Alexei's tender age of three.

"Yes, yes." She was clearly accommodating and let me stay the full three hours for three days in a row. And so we were initiated into life at the Co-op, more fulfilling, supportive, and rich than I had even imagined. It was a true sisterhood, where we worked hand and hand as mothers, committed to a shared devotion to our children—not just to tending them, but teaching them how to think, how to resolve conflict, how to show love, and how to treat the space we shared together.

My chair position would be the garden. Um, what? Garden. Do I want it? Yes! I'll take it.

The woman currently in the garden position really wanted to be the chair of photography. And the other chair positions—auction, stay-and-play coordinator, accounting, marketing, admissions, work-day coordinator, website maintenance—they were all taken. So, gosh! I would be in the garden. That was like sending Br'er Rabbit to the briar patch.

I showed up on my first Saturday maintenance day with some broccoli seedlings from Green Jeans nursery. Not because I knew I would be in the garden that day, but because it was on my way home from school pick-up the day before, and I felt like stopping. And that's what they had. As it turned out, I would be planting. I turned over the soil in the four raised beds, reorganized the irrigation tubes, and planted a late/winter, early/spring bed with broccoli.

Suzy had brought raspberries to plant, and Heather, who had charge of the irrigation from an app on her phone, fell into weeding. So while I dug and planted, we talked and circled, the way women are supposed to do. They kept deferring to me with questions: May I plant this here? Do you want this there? How much time on the irrigation? I paused each time wondering why they were asking me, slow in my assumption of role as Garden Chair. Not as easy or relaxed with my time as they were. I needed to be massaged, like hard winter soil, into an easier, more receptive form where new seeds could plant themselves into me. Everything at the Co-op seemed to be designed to do this: lend a hand, offer support, work together, and soften me into someone who could learn to trust again. To help me slow down and let myself be supported.

 **Purification Sauce** (Sweet Cilantro/Arugula Cucumber dressing) - *cilantro has become famous most recently for its ability to bind heavy metals and remove them from your body. Even those of us who have led healthy lives seem to have trace amounts of metals, from…toothpaste? Paint? Beauty products? Vaccines? It is also said to bring one clarity and direction on one's path. This sauce excites me by the spoonful and even more when I put it on top of a warm corn tortilla with feta or farmers cheese and extra slices of Serrano or jalapeño pepper.*

1 bunch cilantro
1 bunch Arugula (or other dark green leafy vegetable of choice)
1/2 to 1 Persian cucumber
1/2 lemon or lime (juiced)
2 dates (remove pits)
1 tsp apple cider vinegar
1/3 cup olive oil
1/4 cup sunflower oil
1/8 to 1/4 cup water (pour to desired thickness)

Humility
Pinch of salt and cayenne to taste

Rinse the greens and cut into pieces. Place all ingredients in blender, and blend until smooth and creamy. Pour on salads, rice, vegetables. Wrap with cucumber, slices of jalapeño, and walnuts in a leaf of escarole or red leaf or green leaf lettuce. Or dip with apples, with cucumber, with carrots…Dance.

At first, we planted our seeds in the full moon. Maureen requested some garden work with the children. I complied.

"Yes! I just picked up some seed trays and soil the other day. We can plant seeds today," I told her.

We had a giant box of seeds in the tool shed from last year. So I pulled out the ones I knew we could grow here in California in the spring: the green beans and sugar snaps, the carrots, parsnips, kale, mustard greens, radishes, chives maybe….and set up some trays on a table inside that the children could fill with soil and a few seeds during morning activities.

Of course planting with children is a mixture of magic and torture. Them, being at one with the magic of it, and me, being at one with the need for order and carefulness. So we managed to mostly fill the trays and mostly put three to four seeds into each square, with a thin layer of soil on top.

"Did I have some popsicle sticks to mark the seeds?" Maureen wondered.

No, we didn't do that. But I would know what the seedlings were when I saw them, I assured her.

"Ok. Yes. Yes. Ok," she said. She was not at all convinced, but compliant. Trusting.

Next, we put them on the windowsill in the room where they had done it before. But it faced East. So we moved them to the main room where the windows face South. The children enter and exit there every morning. It was an easy place to remember them, watch them, water them. I guess it wasn't much of a surprise in two to three weeks when every square was sprouted and had a happy baby plant there, growing.

What *was* a surprise was how much further along and happier these little plants were than the ones I started at home. Mine, too, faced South. Mine, too, were watered every day and spent days outside in the warm sun and the cold evenings inside. But mine weren't strong and growing as quickly as these ones in the Co-op. What was different? Could the children's laughter, games, energy at the Co-op be enough to make those plants that much more vibrant!? I had certainly heard this theory before.

BELIEVING IN WHAT YOU FEEL

I have heard that Energy Medicine only works if you believe in it. But even my greatest skeptics and critics have become fans of what at first seems like magic, or the way of a witch.

My mother is my most beloved and esteemed convert. She is a woman of great discrimination and values scientific method, Western Medicine, and the proof of what she can see, taste, smell, hear, and touch. But when her neck hurts and will not respond to conventional treatment, she surrenders to my hands.

In them, she finds reprieve. Not because she believes in it, but because she feels it. She feels her neck unwind into the silent listening of my hands when they hold her head. She feels the wave of energy move like fluid along her spine and tease apart the knots in her neck. Often, she says she doesn't feel anything. But still, she's willing to lie there in my hands and let me hold her.

I feel into the cycle of health that moves in invisible arcs, curves, and tides through her spinal column and nervous system. We call it a cranial hold, designed to connect with the rhythm of the cerebrospinal fluid and help the fluid find its long and restorative tide. This is how the healing occurs, through connection and witnessing of the healthy movement. We can't see it though; we can only feel it. Maybe it is the way of the witch…cyclical, unseen, mysterious…and because of all of those things, *magic*.

Often, I find the greatest release from real pain happens without even contact to the body. There is a connection to the energy channels that work from the outside down into the flesh of the human anatomy which releases the stuck energy that is creating the pain. This is power of Spirit as it breathes through form and into the seen objects we have come to rely on.

 **Heal Me Chicken Soup** - *the role of chicken soup in seasonal health and nourishment cannot be disputed. It is handed to us in many shapes and forms and from many places and cultures, and here we embrace it with wonder at its ability to heal. The hen is an ultimate symbol of generosity and nourishment across the ages. Like all medicine, especially those that come from animals, it is "used" with discretion and gratitude.*

4 chicken thighs bone in, skin on
(or whole chicken, gutted, cut in pieces)
1/2 onion
2 cloves garlic, peeled and crushed with side of knife
6 to 8 cups of water
2 zucchini squash or summer squash
2 carrots
1 yucca, peeled and cut into pieces
1 bay leaf
2 tbsp sunflower oil/olive oil
Appetite

Lime and chiles to serve (serrano or jalapeno chiles are not so hard to find, and taste great here).

Heat large stock pot over low to medium heat on stove. Add 2 tbsp of your preferred oil and chicken, already rinsed and dried. Let sear for 3 minutes each side. Add garlic, onion, 6 cups of water. Simmer for 2 or so hours. Add vegetables and cook 20 minutes more. Pour off extra broth into a container to freeze for future use. (Once broth is cool, scrape the fat off of the surface and discard.) When eating the soup, salt to taste, and serve with a generous slice of lime and sliced chiles to give it extra aliveness and zest.

Remi was born in the spring and, like Oliver, in a hospital among a sisterhood of whispers that carried me through the mantra of, "I can't do this anymore." His father was far away the night Remi came, working on a ranch in Oregon. My friend Catherine, mother of one boy and no stranger to the marathon of birth, would be my partner. She came for me at midnight on March 3, 2013.

The hospital would not admit me though. Despite my insistence that he was coming, I showed no signs of active labor. Instead, they put me into what seemed like a dark closet, handed me a cup of ice water, and left. "We'll be back to check on you," the nurse reassured me.

And she was, many times, back to check on me. She was the kind of nurse that made me realize not everybody needs a doula. This, it seemed to me that night, was originally the role of the nurse: to support, to comfort, to advocate for. Perhaps this is where it gets difficult: advocating "for" the mother, when the nurse is ingrained in the "system." She has to comply with the orders and regime of birth in the hospital. Perhaps she doesn't know the negative implications of Pitocin or an epidural. So, she may not have the strength to help you say NO when you need it the most. But this nurse for me that night had just the right amount of heart. She embodied, in a figure as full and fecund as mine, compassion, good listening, and the loveliest form of gentleness. Then, she was unphased by the fierceness required later of a woman giving birth. So she made me think twice about extra birth support.

Finally, even with my water not broken or cervix completely dilated, they moved me to a birthing room. This room was big enough for me to lay out my sheepskin rug and ride the waves of contraction on the ground. That was until the midwife arrived with her own back ache and requested that I get up onto the bed. I didn't move fast enough or stay focused on the task at hand: to get onto the bed. I quickly became a difficult patient and heard Catherine apologizing for me to the team.

Every gesture, every sensation, every impossibility, like climbing up onto the bed during those contractions, was held with me by Catherine. She held my eyes, my arms, my heart. She was close when I needed her to be close and spacious when I needed her to be farther away. She was quiet when I needed quiet, and she whispered when I needed words. In this heroic mirroring that mothers do, selflessly, daily, she helped me bring Remi through in an abbreviated five hours. Like Oliver, he came out with eyes wide open with a thirsty curiosity that only his oldest brother has endless patience for.

We still don't know where my water, Remi's water, went. It never came out. Neither in a trickle, nor in a flood. He slipped out on a path already paved by his brothers, but never washed by our own shared fluids. I still, to this day, wonder where it went. Where did it go?

Remi's father came two days later. He brought me a rooster from the farm in Oregon where he was working.

THE MEDICINE IN A MIRROR

And so I died once more into the becoming of a mother.

I think, given the right attention and reverence, motherhood for even the most independent of us modern women is the quintessential threshold between the Northern shield of responsibility, where we claim authority for our lives, and the Eastern shield of surrender, where we dive deeper into selfless service to a child, a community, or the Divine. If the crossing of this threshold is not met with awareness or ceremony, we are left feeling bereft of all we have lost and hopeless in the intensity of what service to a family really looks like. Sisterhood, and the mirror of the mindful mothers who have come before us, is marvelous medicine in the tired times of early infancy.

 **Warm My Belly Bowl** - *native people across the globe call this congee. Rebecca Wood, the author of some of my favorite cookbooks, describes it as "the Asian equivalent of mother's chicken soup." It is healing and restorative, a therapy unto itself. Like chicken soup, it is adjusted to fit the culture and ingredients on hand. There is a purity to congee, and a depth after cooking grains into water for 6 hours, that is unmatched by other foods. There is no way to eat it quickly. It's not physically possible. So it is truly a slow food that begs one into full presence with their bowl and their body. It is an ideal food following birth, as it restores the yin fluids that are lost in giving birth. It is soothing and will not upset the newborn's tummy when he/she begins to breastfeed, as so many other foods will. It can be made from large grains besides rice, including rye, job's tears, millet, barley, and buckwheat. And, since you can keep grains for months in the cupboard, it does not require a trip to the store.*

1/2 cup rice
6 cups water
1 pinch of salt
Fire

Rinse rice and combine with water in a large stock pot. Place over medium to high heat and bring to a boil. Stir. Reduce to low heat and simmer for approx. 6 hours, stirring occasionally until the grain is partially dissolved into the water, giving it a thick consistency.

For depth or warmth add butter, flax oil, cinnamon, ginger, honey

For iron protein add pinto beans, liver, duck, beef, nettles, watercress

Two weeks later, when the new moon set in, I was reminded of my practice of planting seeds two to three days before the new moon. In our eagerness for a garden class as well as a garden, I had forgotten about Biodynamic Farming and planting in synch with the new moon!! So we set to work again, perhaps a little more carefully this time with what we were planting and where, and made a new set of seedlings.

All variables the same.

Except for the moon.

And I wasn't the only one who noticed that this time they grew even more quickly and a bit stronger.

So it was easy, that morning when Maureen offered me up to teach a garden lesson in our morning circle, to awaken the children's imagination to the possibility that perhaps, just maybe, it is true that the moon in the sky and the stars affect the roots and the plants in the earth. And, as they assert in Biodynamic Farming, planting and harvesting with the cycles of the moon is fundamental to having a healthy, bountiful, and successful garden. We were seeing it right here, with our own little baby plants. This morning, everyone's face lit up, most of all my own, with the privilege of passing these possibilities on to them. Our future gardeners.

"We feed the apple trees just like we feed ourselves. They need minerals and vitamins just like we do," I tell Alexei today as I am pouring the murky seaweed-powder water into the boxes at the base of our apple trees.

"But why?"

"You didn't know that plants need to eat too, did you?" I replied.

I didn't, in fact, until I was 22 and worked in the garden in Guatemala. We went for a field trip one day to learn about hydroponics: the future of growing our food in discarded tires. There, in Sololá Guatemala, I was schooled in just how to get healthy vegetables out of an old, recycled rubber box: constant attention and a steady and controlled supply of concentrated minerals and vitamins.

What I remember most about that day was not our lesson, or the American organization offering it, but just how hot and dry it was! And then, the feeling of traveling by bus with an elderly Mayan woman in her regal costume of handwoven cotton and adjustable wrap skirt. And then, sitting with her in the only restaurant on the town square eating "Caldo de Res," an exquisite bone soup made from boiling beef bones in water for many hours. It was served with green boiled squash, Chayote, and fresh handmade tortillas. Every bite was mouthwatering. Also, that Dona Benita—my companion who walked in service every day to all of us, including her five children and all of their children, including her daughters-in-law, including the garden and the cooperative nursery school where it was, and now including me—got to have lunch in a restaurant. That she got to sit and let somebody else serve her.

"Oh," says Alexei in response to my comment, and he keeps jumping on the trampoline.

Even with this warm and spacious day, half-dressed in the garden and feeding from what I love most, I am tired tonight. That deep leave-me-alone tired that doesn't want anyone to touch her or even be near.

It comes with certain ideas about what I have lost and what I am longing for. Some attention I was getting that now I am not. And I miss it.

Then, there's the energy draining out of me through the idea: I've been foolish. How embarrassing. The thought that I have embarrassed myself just kills me. I can't stand humiliation.

Humiliation, I imagine, is mostly my sense of myself, as everyone else seems to show me compassion and understanding. It's as if I expected myself to be something I am not. It comes with a shadow of fear. Fear of…being seen? Seen for who I really am or what I really want? Who am I anyway?

Meanwhile, Alexei is showering me with kisses or at least wanting to. And Remi, with questions, all of them earnest and intelligent. They would be delightful to a mother who was paying attention. But I am tired now, like the light of this transitional season that has not yet found its full force.

Let's keep dinner simple tonight.

Pasta Please Mom Angel Hair with Greens - *when you're building on last night's dinner and don't have a chance to get to the store, dip into what's already there and flesh it out. This is not left-over, but creative engagement with what is already living there with you. It's efficiency, but also connection and ease, which frees you up to put your attention and your energy where it belongs, in caring for yourself, your family, and the gardens that grow around you. The vegetables here are in my garden and easy for me to harvest, clean, and add to a meal. Choose ones that are easy for you, and play with possibilities.*

1 box angel hair (gluten free optional)
1 bunch asparagus (cooked 5 to 8 minutes in boiling water)
1/2 cup frozen peas
2 heads garlic (peeled and sliced)
2 slices onion (chopped)
1 to 2 tbsp olive oil
Presence
Salt to taste

Bring large pot of water to boil on stove. Add pasta and cook to time specified on package. Drain.

Heat olive oil in large skillet on stove over medium heat. Add garlic, onions, asparagus, and peas, and cook until tender (approx. 5 minutes). Add angel hair and toss together. Serve. Then salt to taste. Or add more olive oil, purification sauce, or apple parsley dressing. (p 122)

Life folds in and out of itself, over and over. Death is the doorway to birth, just as birth brings a mother and family to a symbolic death. Our stories fold into each other again, with the death of Señora Cabrera, my children's Spanish teacher's mother.

"She was holding Meinir's hand," she said. "I was still in Mexico."

Slowly, as she saw I was really listening and came to trust this, slowly she unfolded the story from the tight pocket where she had it stored in her chest and offered it up to me.

"Yes, I had asked her if I should really go to Mexico, as I do every year at this time, and she said yes. She insisted. I knew I had to go."

I nod, keeping my eyes locked into hers, letting her know she is safe with me.

"I think she was waiting for me to go. She didn't want me to be here when she passed. Her spirit was so strong, but her body so fragile already."

After working long days at our school, teaching handwork and Spanish to the children, a job that requires the patience of a saint and the focus of a carpenter, Señora would go home to her mother, who was now 97 years old, had birthed and raised 13 children, and Señora, her daughter, would care for her.

"Oh, it's much harder than being here with the children at school," she would tell me. "Sometimes I am up all night with her needing me for one thing or another."

Señora was not complaining, just painting a picture of what was true. But her mother was gone now, and the light that she had set to come on automatically at night, when her mother needed something, is still programmed to come on. She is not ready to adjust it yet.

"You had many years together," I said to her, smiling.

"Yes, yes we did," she confirmed, a somber but surrendered look on her face.

"Yesterday, when I got home, I called to tell her I was there: Mama! Ya vine," she said. "I am already home." So deeply engrained was her habit of calling to her mother when she got home. These are the habits to keep, I thought. The strings that keep us attached.

She told me more story, unpacking it piece by piece. About Meinir, the director of this school where we are now, going to get flowers before she went to her bedside at the hospital so that Señora's mother would have flowers to smell in her final moments. Even before Señora had asked Meinir for permission to go get flowers, as she intended to do, Meinir had already gone for them. She talked about Meinir holding her one hand on one side of the bed, and her son, Milton, who taught here at our school in the kindergarten, holding the other. About speaking to her on the phone just before she died, and then again, about the scent of the flowers that had carried her off.

"I think it's not how we think it is," she says to me then. "That death is just an instant. That they are here one minute, and the next minute they are not. No. Death is slow. It takes us one step at a time."

"Mmmmm. Yes. That is what I have heard," I reply. "Es un camino. It is a walk, isn't it?"

"Yes," she agrees, allowing some dreaminess into her countenance. Yes. And then all of the paperwork to file. All of the obligations of reporting her death, paying taxes, attending to the legal formalities of it. That is what she did when she got home. She hasn't touched her mother's room yet, to rearrange or give away her belongings. It's not quite time for this yet. No, not yet.

Other parents are starting to come into the room now. It's time for school to begin. Some have flowers, an orchid, or a cake to give her. Some are merely trying to keep up with the daily details of managing their children. A man's voice calls for morning circle. It's time for Señora to go now.

The body has been attended to, the paperwork submitted, the bills all paid. Señora is back now, to carry the song of life along for the children who look forward to her class every day. It's the class where they are asked not to sit still, but to move their bodies and use their hands. They are taught that they develop their brains by knitting, a repetitive gesture that requires the hands to meet and cross at the mid-line, the center. This helps in the formation of neuronal connections between the two sides of the brain—left brain and right brain. These connections help not only in the formation of balanced brain, but also in creating physical balance in the body. And then, it's fun! Plus, they learn they are valued here not only for something they say or don't say and think or don't think, but for making something with their hands.

Music is coming out of morning circle. It does every morning. It keeps the impulse of joy for life chasing at the heels of every certain death, and it is an essential part of elementary school.

For the children, it's fun. For the parents, we know they are learning to be strong and confident in voice.

I am reminded of the Bar Mitzvah that Oliver and I went to on Sunday. The way that every teaching and comment exploded into joyous song when it finished. Who is that man!? I thought, every time he launched a song into the space. And who is the woman next to him?

"Are there two Rabbis?" I asked Oliver, thinking that California might be leading the way in partnering male/female at the altar. "Do they call it an altar in the Synagogue?" The man singing, his voice connects the space in the room with some kind of light lasso, making the air thick and nourishing, like Diego the Brazilian Capoeira teacher at Alexei's school. With just a tambourine, the quality of his voice, and the melody in his lungs, he fills the entire pre-school with something like liquid gold.

"It's the Hazzan," Oliver tells me, relaxed and confident in his response.

"How do you know?" I ask him.

"They told us," he replies easily. Hmmmm. I missed that. "A Hazzan is a Jewish musician or presenter trained in the vocal arts who helps lead the congregation in songful prayer."

There are so many things I do not know about this religion, even with Oliver's grandmother being "Jewish." But she is an atheist Jew and does not believe in God or self-help. Believe it or not, we are terribly fond of each other. We both believe in France, good food, and complex, intelligent literature.

The ceremony, however, is familiar. The elements of the Holy are like the ones I know from the Episcopal Church where I grew up and the Buddhist ones I embraced as a young adult who gave up God when He took her big brother in a snorkeling accident. I know them, too, from the Catholic Church of Latin America, a place where church is fecund and fertile, even in the austerity of its regimen. There, like the people, the church coughs in flowers, and on the other side of the most sentimental tears and heartbreak you've ever heard, an ecstatic joy is waiting to jump out. And the ceremonies, even the ones given in loss and mourning, still smell like tree resin.

Here in this synagogue there are doors on every side to capture the feeling of a tent, where the Jews used to celebrate the Holy. Even the roof is pitched like the roof of a tent, and the doors are almost as wide as the walls, which are intentionally designed that way to welcome all to prayer. This keeps the outside close to us and makes being inside feel more Holy and bearable to me. It's very different from the thick stone walls where I used to be asked to pray.

So Evan "comes of age" somewhere between music and prayer, friends and family, in the inside of a synagogue and sunlit garden. Somewhere between a commitment to Judaism and one to celebration with his eighth grade friends who are not there now, but will be there for the party tonight.

Rainbow Flower Salad - *the sharp and peppery taste of these leaves is so original and alluring. I feel them dance on my tongue and make me want more. I harvest them from the garden, which tells me they carry the nutrients of this soil, this sunshine, this air, and the blessing of my presence when I water them. This is the added nutrition.*

> *I bunch nasturtium leaves and flowers*
> *1 bunch mixed salad greens*
> *Olive oil*
> *Rice wine vinegar (seasoned)*
> *Seasonal fruit (plums, early peaches, or nectarines)*
> *Hope*
> *Salt to taste*

Rinse and dry the nasturtium leaves. Fold into your other greens, and massage with olive oil and vinegar of choice. Add fruit of season (late summer peaches, apples, raisins). Salt to flavor, if needed. Delight in the unique experience of eating your garden leaves and flowers.

THE SPIRIT OF LOSS

There is something about the ceremony of crossing a threshold that makes the crossing more relevant, real, bearable. I say bearable because I have noticed how reluctantly I move from one stage to another. It's not something I am conscious of while it's happening, only later looking back. Like choosing girlhood over womanhood, and not stepping with hunger and wholeness through adolescence. Or choosing freedom over marriage, and vice-versa.

Moving through modern times is an amazing exercise in choice. Especially in the West of the United States, we keep rewriting the rules. Rules about how we live, how we think, how we see, how we function as individuals and as a community. As we try to reclaim ancient ways of all cultures, we re-think the traditions and ceremonies of the culture already in place. It is a unique arrival point in our freedom as a people. But I have noticed how completely I have let go of all ceremonies and the structures that once held me. There is an emptiness now and a rootlessness that is looking to root. I am reminded of a newborn suckling his mother's breast— we call it "rooting" when he hammers his head against his mother's breast in search of milk.

Beautiful ritual is so essential to mark the passages of one state of being from another. It's how we mirror our children, no matter what age they are, and beckon them into 'becoming,' into assuming the unimaginable responsibility of what it is to grow up and become teachers and leaders for their own children. Without right ritual in the places where it belongs, our true triumphs—the letting gos and the claimings—are lost.

In the center of the backyard behind the Co-op, there is a gigantic, ancient pine. It seems to set the tone for the entire playground. It says, in no uncertain terms, I am anchored here. This is my home. Nothing else wants to grow back there. Even the shade-loving plants have a short and uncelebrated run.

"I have tried to grow everything back here. Anything!" Maureen says one day.

But nothing else will grow. They say it is the oil in the pine needles. Funny how we still keep trying though.

Tomorrow, they will deliver a truck load of fresh sand for the gigantic wood frame beneath the pine. Its roots are buried beneath it, like treasures for the children to dig up with shovels.

"We'll pull out the shovels and rakes, and let them all help even it out. It will be good work for them," Maureen said.

Everybody noticed the following day when the children, so deeply engaged in their work, all played better together. They argued less and needed less. They focused more and delighted in the mission of spreading the sand.

There were other jobs to do, too, as the following day was an open house and new prospective families would be visiting. We had to hang tape on the low rafters of the treasure ship. And to sweep it. We needed to wipe down the chalkboards and dry erase play stations and hang the crafts up on the wall. We needed to water the potted plants in the front garden and pick plums from the tree. With so many parents to oversee the children, the day unfolded with ease and grace, and I wondered, why don't we give the kids real jobs every day?

Even children need this sense of purpose. Yes, play has its purpose, especially when it mirrors real life work. But children know when their work is relevant and when it's not. And they are so proud when they do something that they know really helps.

Some days I see how much easier it is to be home with them folding laundry, doing dishes, sweeping the floor, making the beds. Staying connected to them inside of the chores. Handing Alexei a broom when I am sweeping. Letting Remi put on my dishgloves and fill the sink with warm bubbles when there are dishes. This is how to keep their hands in it. And how I keep my relationship with them from becoming conversation about what we did, what we want, what we are going to do.

Some days it feels ordinary and too hard to organize them, coordinate them, or clean up after them.

But when we get to vacation and my big boys don't know what to do with themselves, I think it's because I never taught them. They were busy shuttling back and forth to their dad's. Going to soccer practice and games. Planning for and going to playdates with friends somewhere else. Now, they're not quite sure what to do with themselves at home…and I'm not going to accept that this is just a "boy thing."

VIBRATIONAL MEDICINE

There's a flower from a mythical plant called Cat's Claw that is supposed to help us know when to engage and when to disengage. Just a few drops of this essence on the tongue, repeated over the day and through the week, gives us the ability to discern when to get involved and when to step away. When to fight, or when to not fight. In other words, choose our battles with discretion and integrity. And thus, this flower can help protect us in our relationships. All of this gets communicated simply through the vibration of the flower. (desertalchemy.com)

Um, what?

It's not aromatherapy or an herbal tincture. Though as an herb, in tincture, or in capsule form, Cat's Claw is believed to have curative properties equivalent to an anti-viral, anti-biotic, and even anti-parasitic (Anthony William, 2016, *Life-Changing Foods*). As such, it is effective in reducing everything from inflammation, which William suggests is caused by undiagnosed viruses and bacteria, to healing digestive disorders, neurological symptoms, and eliminating parasites. It is then a miracle cure, which he insists should be at the heart of each of our medicine cabinets.

And I, a willing subject, would second. This plant, like so many, has numerous applications. It is all-potent and has the potential to make us feel better. This is without having to go through the battery of tests that are required in our allopathic medical models to try to figure out why our systems are haywire, tracking symptoms like a mad rat down into dead-end tunnels, and finding ourselves in the end exhausted and sicker than we began, only with entirely new sets of symptoms.

But this lesson is about the flower essence, not its herbal remedy. A plant that, in its vibrational form, has the ability to teach us or show us how to engage or disengage in healthy ways. But how!? Not through discourse. Or conversation. Or practice. But through its vibrational composition…it teaches and helps you embody your self, your being. Um, what?

My experience is that the Sacred Geometry inherent in the anatomy of a flower transfers itself into the water, and then through the water solution into your body. The extensive studies by author, businessman, and consciousness studies pioneer Masaru Emoto 2005, suggest that water organizes or disorganizes its molecular pattern according to the energy, vibration, or thought pattern in the field (Masara Emoto, 2005, *The Hidden Messages in Water*). So, the sacred geometrical pattern in the flower is translated into the solution called a flower essence, and then on a molecular level into your body. Your body is between 60% water for an adult and 75% water for a child and would, according to Emoto's research, respond on a molecular level to the pattern held in the flower essence. In your body it has the potential to permeate your own fluid cells and help re-organize their structure to your own sacred blueprint or highest potential. This is the highest form of harmony or organization that your cell structure is capable of and, in my experience, feels like light, ease, and peace. This is the magic of a flower essence.

Candace Pert's research on *The Molecules of Emotion* further support this idea, that a vibration, such as a feeling, translates on a molecular level into your cell structure and thereby plays a significant role in your health. Pert's research shows that the external walls of cells are covered with receptors that are coded to receive specific molecules we call peptides. These molecules simultaneously communicate on all levels of the bodymind, from our minds and emotions and through our immune systems and digestive tracts. So, while your brain is receiving information and processing it through the structural highway of your nervous system, other parts of your body, including your gut and its organs, are also receiving this information and processing it directly, without instruction from your brains or your nervous system. Pert's research debunks the belief that our mind is separate from the functioning of our body and paves the way for the revolutionary field in medicine called Psychoneuroimmunology that I described on page 18, and touch in on again at the end of the book.

So, like this morning when I was desperate again to brush my three-year-old's teeth, and he was resisting again, in a great theatrical display which repeats itself, over and over, could I use this flower essence? To help me know when to step away and when to persist?

Or with my teenager, who I am arguing with, again, to get up out of bed and move his body in the morning instead of lying there and reading? Occupying his mind and paralyzing his body before the daylight has even had a chance to work itself through his limbs, could I use this essence to know when to step away and when to persist? When "to engage, or disengage."

I think it may be for more severe acts of engagement and disengagement. How to know when it's healthy to get involved. Or not. When one should step away. How to know what is worth fighting for and what is not. But imagine, if we can come to this knowing somewhere inside of us, through felt sense or intuition, instead of getting tangled up in argument or reason. Instead of becoming locked into questions, we have a feeling in our bodies. It's clear, and light, and simple. That's what flower essences do for me. They simply help me know. Clearly, in my body. What is true, and what is not.

I use them when I feel dark or uncertain. Despondent. Weary. Or Alone. Over-whelmed or tired. Confused or not clear. Just a few drops on my tongue throughout the day (instead of a piece of gum, a kombucha, or any other oral distraction). I can use a flower essence.

Then usually, within a day or two, I notice I feel lighter. Easier. More fluid in my steps and more connected in my relationships. I don't always notice it at first. It requires pausing and paying attention. I have to remember into what I was feeling a few days earlier. And it is easy to forget. But when I do it, I am dumbstruck, amazed. In awe at just how simple 'feeling better' can be. That no one had to listen, or explain, or construct a narrative or an apology. No one had to suffer my doubts with me. I just feel better.

I like to tell people that in Argentina and Germany, flower essences are sold in the pharmacy. They are put together by the pharmacists, the way prescription drugs are filled here in the United States. There, they are already recognized as real medicine or medicinal remedies. That alone is enough for me to say Hey! Wait! Stop! Look at this!! It can be easy. And clean. And connected. And real.

I have now used them for 20 years.

Flower Essence List - some examples (Kaminski and Katz, *Flower Essence Repertory*)

> **Golden Yarrow** - helps one remain open to others, while maintaining a sense of inner-protection and sensitivity.

> **Hibiscus** - integration of soul warmth and bodily passion, particularly with female sexuality.

> **Larch** - helps restore self-confidence, free creative potential, and inspire self-expression.

Olive - for extreme fatigue. Helps one to reach across physical resources and connect to the metaphysical energy that truly sustains the body.

 Rock Rose - for courage in extreme circumstance.

Walnut - a remedy for times of great life transition.

White Chestnut - for extreme mental agitation. Helps calm and clear the mind.

Wild Oat - helps one find his/her true life purpose or vocation. Restores energy and life force through connection to purpose.

 Make Me Hum Jasmine Tea - *the smell of jasmine in the spring is perhaps as alluring and exciting as the taste of this tea. It awakens and excites, offering something more than the gentle caffeine that is in the green tea beneath the jasmine flowers. There is a smile that comes with the buzz from this tea that seems to last me longer than any cup of caffeine. And so, I often forget to let this tea go when spring falls away, and I drink it all year.*

1 tbsp jasmine tea
1 to 2 cups hot water

Bring water to a boil. Let rest and slightly cool. Pour over jasmine leaves and let sit 5 to 7 minutes. Pour off and enjoy. For a short cut, pour approximately 1 tbsp of cool water over the tea leaves before you pour the boiling water. This prevents you from burning the delicate green tea and preserves the purity and delicacy of taste.

"Mom. What should I do?" says Rafa.

We are sitting in the car at 5 pm on a Friday night, waiting for Oliver to complete his hour-long breakdancing class.

"I don't know. Nothing. I am going to close my eyes and just rest. You could join me."

"No."

"Hmm. Well, you're welcome to get out of the car and go for a walk."

"Boring."

"You can go in and watch Oliver."

"Stupid. This is boring."

"Rafa. You can get out of the car and walk in any direction and find life. Some kind of adventure. Some possibility of magic. You may run into a friend. I don't know. Just go!!"

"No. That all sounds dumb."

"Ok. You come up with an idea then."

"Can you give me some money?"

There is a wonderful grocery store up the street, and I imagine he would like to go get himself a treat.

"No. You just had a good snack, and we will eat dinner as soon as we get home. What about walking up to the creek!? It's just a block away."

He lights up, a little. "Could you drive me?"

"I'm not going to drive you!! It's just a block away."

"Then I'm not going."

"Ok. Suit yourself."

"Would you go with me?" he asks. Ahhhh. We have a breakthrough here.

"Yes. After I rest. I would love to go with you. Thanks for asking."

But he is not content with that answer, with having to wait, with the whole scenario of not being entertained or provided for. His body is screaming some language of defeat. He looks like a plant without water in the hot sun, wilting and limp. It's as if his will and curiosity are gone. Fled. I remember all of the times he wanted something he couldn't have…his response was always, "Fine, I don't care." He seemed then to banish his "caring."

"Fulfillment seeks a garden, fertile and wild, teeming with creepers and creatures, tangles and thorns." —**Ushi Patel**

But still, I won't move my line. I am tired and need to rest before I can go another step.

His feet find their way to the console between the two front seats. They are flopping at me, on purpose. "Rafa, please stop." He pushes again. "Rafa, let me rest! Just another few minutes."

His leg comes up against my shoulder, clearly to agitate and annoy me. "Rafa! Stop!" But he pushes again. Until I push back. Literally.

And then, he explodes, "I hate you, and I never want to see you again!"

He shouts in no unclear terms. Then he gets out of the car and goes away.

Did I do something wrong?

But the part of me that is used to imploding refuses to collapse this time. My answer is no. I didn't do anything wrong. I held a line with a 10-year-old that had to be held. Whatever happens, I did what I, as a parent, was supposed to do.

Would he run away? Would he come back? What happens if the class ends and I can't find him? I remember my mother navigating these rocky terrains with my brother. I remember him "running away" and coming back, and my mother staying strong throughout it. I envision her strength, her clarity, and his un-compromised devotion to her in the end. So, I breathe. I remember Justine last week insisting how important it is for parents to hold their lines and to set clear boundaries so that children know that the container is solid and safe. Yes, it was ok that I didn't give in. It was even ok that I pushed back.

I get out now and walk to the creek. But why did Rafa act so defeated? So indifferent? So incapable of just getting out of the car and going to explore? It was as if his power had been "turned off."

He came back with his brother 30 minutes later with ease and softness. He came back surrendered and loving. I realized then just how tired he was.

Then, 24 hours later, our power went out. Literally. PG&E imposed a county-wide grid shutdown on Marin. All of the power was out, and there was nothing anybody could do about it.

"It won't happen. This is just politics," said one neighbor.

"How can they do this!?!?" exclaimed another.

"Come over and have some salmon. I am lighting the grill and am going to cook up all the fish," offered yet another.

Everyone had a different way of meeting this new form of powerlessness. Some seemed completely defeated and were driving around the neighborhood in the morning, looking for somewhere to get hot coffee. Others just wanted to get over the bridge and into San Francisco, where the power was still on.

"All of the hotel rooms in the city are booked," Eleanor, a neighbor and trusted source of information, told me. She and I were happy to be home still in our pajamas and witnessing the fall out of what happens to a village when their lines of communication and comfort get cut.

Oliver was convinced that this was the worst day of his life. "I HATE everything about this day," he exclaimed. It was only 10 am. But his throat hurt, he was in and out of a fever, his nose was congested, and his coughing insistent. "This sucks!! It all sucks."

They had canceled his overnight camping trip with his friends due to questionable air quality from nearby fires, and he felt not just bad, but aimless. Angry. Distraught.

"Oliver, you don't even feel well. It is a perfect day to be inside and rest. Get better." I said to him. It didn't help.

"Oliver, get off the phone please. Let's save the power for our essential communications."

This made him even madder! He exploded into a fit of coughing and had to go outside. Is the coughing a reaction to the fires? Last year when the fires tore through Northern California and we weren't even allowed to leave our houses, all of my children fell ill.

"At least we're all here, safe and together," I tried, one more time, to make it better.

But nothing made it better. Nothing could. Later, looking back, I could see that no matter what, he was going to feel bad. He was committed to it, to feeling bad. And the best I could have done was to let him.

He was angry, like the teenagers who tore down our street later that night as the sun was setting, yelling and knocking over garbage cans. And I imagine they have a lot to be angry about, given the illusions of power and safety they have been fed their entire lives.

"I can't believe they can do this!" Oliver insisted. "How can they do this!?"

I explain to him about living on the grid. I remind him about the fire danger.

"It's so dry. One spark and a gigantic fire could strike and spiral out of control. It's supposed to be for our own protection."

"But is it?" he says in his disbelieving way.

"I don't know." I truly don't know.

I do know that at dusk, the street is quiet, and the four of them take out our diverse collection of hockey sticks to play hockey in the street.

"How can this be the first time we have played hockey in the street!?" I asked them later, seeing that their delight with it is as thick and palpable as mine.

Remi chimes in, "Usually there are too many cars."

We eat again by candlelight, and bathe too, in the dim light of mostly dark rooms lit by a candle. The neighbor has a charcoal grill going and insists that we come over for the salmon he had caught the day before. The boys grab the mini-marshmallows and sticks, and we walk over.

"You know, this day has turned out to be really good in the end," Oliver confides in me.

He comes to life beside the fire, in the company of some other young and thoughtful men. And I am tenderized again, to the medicine of the village, holding, massaging, softening, feeding, and healing us all.

Balance My Life Dandelion and Bibb Salad - *dandelion greens are not only wonderful for the liver in the springtime, when it is waking up and clearing winter malaise, it is also potent on a spiritual and emotional level, helping one to reclaim or reconnect the disparate pieces of the Self (Anthony William). This salad balances the bitterness of this awakening green gift, dandelion, with the mellow comfort of Bibb lettuce. Then add the spice of the detoxifying and delicious cilantro dressing, creating the perfect balance of flavors needed to satiate your hunger on every level and in every dimension.*

A handful of dandelion greens, from somewhere not too close to the road. Where dogs don't pee and plants aren't breathing too much exhaust.

> *Bibb lettuce, a head from someone's garden*
> *1 carrot sliced into 2 sides (to crunch with your front teeth but not break them)*
> *Humor*
> *Purification Sauce (p 64)*

Rinse and dry greens. Combine in bowl and smother with dressing. Eat. Sing.

DETOXIFY, PURIFY

The dandelion in the spring is but a reminder that it is time to detoxify your body. It is relentless...in the garden, on the side of the road, at the edge of a dirt field, and there, amidst the grasses on the green baseball field. Western Nutrition, Ayurveda, Chinese Medicine,

Polarity, and now basic common sense call us to lighten the physical load of winter with some cleansing.

But there is something here in the diets and systems of body focus that is getting lost. Something I keep hearing and trying to think or push my way through. A basic principle, now included in integrated forms of psychotherapy, that goes like this:

Feel your feelings

It's an essential piece to letting go, moving on, and now I will qualify as detoxifying. To simply feel your feelings. For many of you, this may be painfully obvious. For me, it is more difficult, and I will call it the feminine face of God.

Feminine, because it is feeling. Like in the Chinese System where the yin is the feminine, receptive, feeling nature of things. Yang, then, is the action-oriented, directed, masculine face of things. Together they create a balance. Something that is whole. For health and wholeness, they most both exist with equal strength and presence.

This is what it feels like when I finally cry. Divine release. A great relief. Like something that is clinging through me and has claws lodged deep inside, perhaps even deeper than my guts, lets go. Once the water moves and carries with it the debris, perhaps of generations ago, I move somewhat closer to here. Here, closer to a feeling I call "God." It is full presence with just 'what is.'

Most of the time, I am holding it together. Getting boys wiped, dressed, brushed, shoed, shuttled, organized, connected, fed, pacified, instructed, wound down, heard, listened to, wiped, dried, brushed, fed again, and to bed. But sometimes, when the tears finally come, all of the doing ceases, and I can meet with my being. This, to me, is Divine.

"That doesn't sound good?" I ask Oliver

"No," he replies

"What about vermicelli noodles with tofu?"

"No, I don't like vermicelli."

"Ok."

"You see! This. Is what I can't stand about restaurants," he exclaims. "I'm going outside."

Yes, I did see. I saw the frustration. The defeat. The betrayal. His powerlessness. I saw how when I said, "No, we aren't going to design our own dishes. We are going to keep it simple and eat what they are offering on the menu," I left him stranded, with no place to go. I saw how I could call him:

picky

difficult

spoiled

ridiculous

for not finding anything on a menu of 200 items at the Vietnamese restaurant.

But instead, I remembered how I felt, and sometimes feel now, when I cannot possibly be nourished by the 1001 things offered up for nourishment before me. Over and over when I was his age, 13, that which they gave me had no resonance or connection for me, and I knew in my bones it wouldn't agree with me. I was made to feel impossible, particular, picky, spoiled, and, in the end, powerless. So I learned how to "not receive." Better to just do it all myself.

Yes, I can see.

"I can tell that he really does want a lot of the things you are asking about," says Rafa when Oliver steps outside.

Rafa has been watching Oliver's face as he reads the menu, as little brothers tend to do: study their older brothers carefully.

"Hmmm," is all I can reply.

Oliver comes back in and opens the menu again. Then closes it, defeated.

"What if you share mine? It's just soup with vermicelli and chicken. Super simple. Then you can get a boba tea that you are wanting. Or spring rolls?"

"No," he says. On the verge of tears.

"Ok." My neutrality here is new for me. Just to let him be emotional and upset and not respond with my own feelings about it. This is new territory, and it feels good.

"I'm going to the car," he tells us and leaves again.

Our food comes. We're eating when he comes back in. Eventually he picks up a fork and plunges it into the bowl of noodles in front of him. But he wasn't able to bring the bite to his mouth. So I did it for him. And he let me.

This was the victory.

That he was still able and willing to receive a bite of food from me. I can't remember the last time I let somebody put a bite of food in my mouth, and when I did, it is because I was deeply, profoundly, utterly in love.

So when I am told, "Don't feed him!! He is 3 now, or 6, or 12, or 13, and old enough to feed himself, I may not listen. Because these gestures of love and receptivity are at the heart of how we give and how we receive. Without them, we will not get fed, be nourished, or find ways to heal. And when someone says, "Feed me!" I hope I will stop and listen…listen closely and watch carefully enough to see what this child is really wanting. Yes! He can feed himself. And I can feed him, too.

A few bites of soup made it better. I don't think it was the soup though.

And in the car, on the way home, Oliver said, "Thank you mom. Thank you so much. For everything. Thank you."

"For what?" I asked him, hearing a tenderness and ease in his voice that I wanted to name.

"For everything."

"For the food? The mango Boba? For understanding?"

"Yes, for the food."

"Ok. I thought you meant for understanding."

"Yes, I did," he said gently. And we went home for a night where neither of them would leave my side.

Running Smoothly Now Celery and Dates - *Anthony William is my hero. Not only has he reclaimed the emotional/spiritual aspect of food, but he has given me back celery and introduced me to dates. No longer "dietetic" or "hippie alternatives," but now 'the way.' As potent and relevant as Loa Tzu's Tao te Ching, they are 'the way' to a healthy gastrointestinal tract, balanced blood sugar, and a clear, incisive mind. Celery can also clear fear, defensiveness, shock, and nervousness from the system, claims William.*

1 head celery
1 cup dates
Excitement
Apple parsley dressing (optional) (p 122)

Wash and chop outer stalks of celery into 2 pieces. Put in cup of water in fridge to grab on demand and eat with a date or 2. Dip in the apple parsley dressing for added sumptuous experience and delight.

A VISION OF WHOLENESS

What if, in the end, it's not about the food? What if, in the end, it's all about the food? These are the kind of paradoxes that reality asks us to come to terms with. The kinds of truths that illuminate the Eastern shield of elderhood. When we understand that it's all true in the end, we release ourselves into the simple privilege of being alive. The simple, yet most complex and divine privilege of being alive, and of learning about love. They are both true.

It's like that when relationships fall apart, too. All of the things that didn't work come to light, and one starts to doubt that they were even loved or witnessed at all. Reconciliation and restitution come only when one remembers that the love was true, too. All of the places where you did connect and share the divine experience of understanding and partnership were as real as the impossibility of it.

When we meet our nourishment with a felt sense, we open the door to deeper balance and stability. Such are the truths of a spiritual reality, where what we feel and what we know direct how we think and behave. Coming to wholeness after falling apart is an extreme process in making room for all of it. It is a long journey if one strives to wrap the mind around it all. Letting go, feeling, making space, and choosing peace, joy, and fulfillment are the short cut.

It is inside the breadth of paradox that we discover the gift of the Eastern shield and its role in how we come to wholeness.

Chlorella is an excellent supplement to take in the spring, when your liver is begging for support. It fortifies and purifies the blood, which assists the liver in its function of detoxification. This helps you feel more emotionally stable, peaceful, and grounded. It helps keep your hormones balanced, your skin clear, your allergies at bay, your blood sugar balanced, and your immune system strong.

"Where have I come from, where did you pick me up?" the baby asked its mother.

She answered, half crying, half laughing, and clasping the baby to her breast,-

"You were hidden in my heart as its desire, my darling.

You were in the dolls of my childhood's games; and when with clay I made the image of my god every morning, I made the unmade you then.

You were enshrined with our household deity, in his worship I worshipped you.

In all my hopes and my loves, in my life, in the life of my mother you have lived.

In the lap of the deathless Spirit who rules our home you have been nursed for ages.

When in girlhood my heart was opening its petals, you hovered as a fragrance about it.

Your tender softness bloomed in my youthful limbs, like a glow in the sky before the sunrise.

Heaven's first darling, twain-born with the morning light, you have floated down the stream of the world's life, and at last you have stranded on my heart.

As I gaze on your face, mystery overwhelms me; you who belong to all have become mine.

For fear of losing you I hold you tight to my breast.

What magic has snared the world's treasure in these slender arms of mine?"

~Rabindranath Tagore

CHAPTER FOUR

RESINA DEL PIÑON

SAP FROM THE PIÑON TREE

The Southern Shield

Youth

SUMMER

Our inner fire, just like the fire outside of us, peaks in the summer. The desire and need to move heightens and, if we are connected inside and out, it insists that we respond. It is time to be outside, to move, to interact, to play. To delight and engage. To choose foods that support feeling light. Greens, fruits, grilled meats, salads. Foods that cool and keep the inner fires in balance.

THE ELEMENTS AS TEACHERS

The journey clockwise continues as we shift out of the Eastern shield and into the Southern shield, home to the fire element. Fire, and the birth of new beginnings. At home in the South, the unselfconscious joy of curiosity and embodiment finds its place.

FIRE

Fire is the element of transmutation—of taking something and transforming it, alchemically, into something else. In our bodies, it is responsible for transforming food into nutrients and energy to feed our muscles, bones, and brains. In our minds, fire takes our lived experiences and lessons and transmutes them to illumination medicine. Fire teaches us the possibility of clearing away the old and stepping into the new. With fire, we learn that our desire is the fuel for finding the truest path in our life. Yes, even the heat of passion is an indication for which way to go. There is danger when it burns out of control. But if we can learn to see it for what it is, energy pushing you to claim your true way, then we can work with the elemental gift that fire offers.

"Delight is a Spiritual practice." —**Morgan Day Cecil**

The awareness is simple at first: I am here. In New Mexico. It is…Breathtaking? Simple? No, not simple. It's wild and alive. I feel ignited by its purity, the dialectic and extremity of it all. It's hot and cold, soft and spikey all at the same time.

I climb out of the tent into the emerging light. The children are still asleep, sort of. I'll just go for a short walk down the dirt road.

Moccasins?
Sneakers?
Moccasins?
Sneakers?

Duh Merrill, moccasins.

I tie the supple second skin onto my awakening feet and climb up out of the tent and into the circle of trees between two running streams that we call a campsite. But I still have this simple idea: this is beautiful.

Then, I remember. I remember to say "Hello." Hello to the wildflowers, the grasses and their tufts of seeds, the struggling cacti and their summer flowers, the piñon trees and their fallen branches. The larkspur, the phlox, the wild mint, the oaks, the rocks, and the butterflies. Just a hello, and suddenly I feel their aliveness. Their breath intermingled here with my own. And what was an idea a moment ago is now a sensation: joy, connection, aliveness, and excitement. The idea that "this is beautiful" has been transformed.

Now, the beauty is deep and rich and in my body. The excitement is increasing, and my challenges—that the bed was too soft and the pillow too big, that I'm tired and anxious—start to let go. The places that are tight and stuck and uncomfortable in my body, I see them now. I can move them, and stretch them, and breathe into them instead of resisting or being mad about them. And because I let myself feel, breathe, and accept them, I can let them go.

If we can't let those places go, we can't really even feel—ourselves, our bodies, or the pulsation of life in the landscape around us. If we can't let go, then it doesn't really matter what we eat or how we exercise or what medicines or tinctures we take. We aren't able to receive them. First, we must be able to feel. We must be able and willing to feel it all.

I stop, somewhere along the quiet road. Everyone, except a crow and a squirrel and a beetle crossing the road, seems to still be sleeping. I let my feet go down into the ground. Then my knees, hips, sacrum, spinal column, left shoulder, elbow, wrist, hand. Pause. I feel already so different in my left side. Heavier. Let go. Right shoulder, elbow, wrist, hand, face, eyes. I pause again. Feel. The achiness is still there. But so is the excitement to see what is just off the trail up the dirt road. The hum of the cicadas is growing, so I'll walk up that way.

Excitement, joy, aliveness. I am reminded of walking into a room where I know somebody, and love him. The feeling that drives me to seek the company of a beloved. A drive toward all social life and relationship.

Now, I propose this: that this human connection, and the bliss that comes with it, is actually possible here too, outside. In these wild, untamed landscapes where trees plant themselves.

"Plant themselves?!" Remi, my six-year-old exclaims. "But how?"

Their parents drop their seeds into the ground. The soil receives them. And the rains and snows water them until they're standing there like those enormous Butterscotch pines (that's what we call the Ponderosa, for the sweet, burnt milk scent in its bark) you see all around you. They're very different from the domesticated trees we live with, I tell him.

That makes him quiet for a delicious moment.

That's the way we find our way to silence in the best of times. "Listening," I call it. Not the effort of meditation or "being quiet" where sometimes, when we are learning, we "try" and we block out stimulation, activity, and distraction around us. We become rigid in the idea that these are distractions. No, this is the listening where we, quiet and open, feel *into*, and then feel from our ears, our hearts, our skin. We notice and pay attention to these sounds and stimulations around us. And then, we shift our observation from those things we can see and hear to the *silence*. We listen to the silence. And we listen with our ears, our hearts, our skin, our bodies. This is "meditation." And where the magic lives. And, if you're a mother, the delicious relief of grace and quiet.

Relief that it's quiet.

And grace of knowing that your kids are engaged with that which is holding them up. The Force that is feeding and breathing life into us all.

This symbol from the *I Ching* offers just the right reflection for these moments of simple grace.

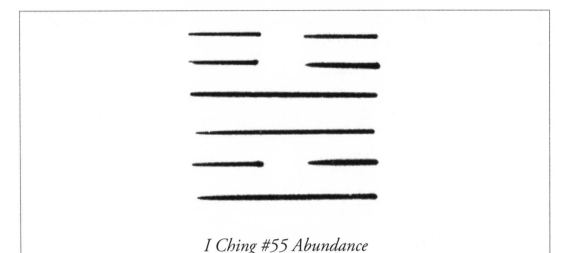

I Ching #55 Abundance

Abundance is the Symbol of grace and prosperity. It indicates a time of great clarity and energy to encounter even the greatest of tasks. While the Symbol abundance suggests a time of advance and progress, one is reminded that in human affairs, as in nature, abundance will give way to its opposite. Use this time to observe and practice how your inner nature lights the way and illuminates the path not just for yourself, but for those around you as well.

MEDICINE AS A FLUID SYSTEM

The emergence of Quantum Physics has completely overturned what we once thought to be true about the atom—the most basic building block of all living matter, including the cell of a body. An atom, once thought to be a fixed, discreet particle of matter, is now believed to be matter in motion. It is not fixed and unchanging, but rather moving and fluid. It fluctuates between states of being...particle and wave. Hence, the atom is a state of being within a spectrum of potential. This very concept overturns how we see matter and challenges the basic premises upon which modern medicine is conceived and practiced.

Older forms of medicine, however—including Ayurveda, Chinese Medicine, Yogic practices, Homeopathic Medicine, and forms of energy healing such as Therapeutic Touch and Medical Qigong—are based upon this very reality, that matter has the ability to completely transform itself, and states of illness that we believe are fixed or finite are not really fixed at all. Which means, in any given moment, the body is a potential, and illness is simply a state.

Quantum Physics also suggests that there is an entire spectrum for intervention, from the most physical intervention on a material level, such as a surgery or strong drug, to intervention on an etheric level, such as prayer or off-the-body touch. This is the spectrum I see that runs from Earth Medicine to Energy Medicine, with modalities on both ends and some that meet into middle:

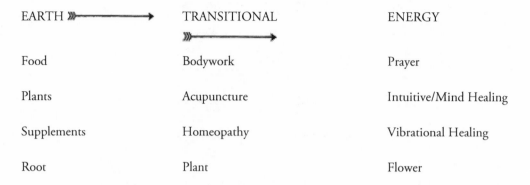

EARTH	TRANSITIONAL	ENERGY
Food	Bodywork	Prayer
Plants	Acupuncture	Intuitive/Mind Healing
Supplements	Homeopathy	Vibrational Healing
Root	Plant	Flower

What is happening in the space between wave and particle? What influences something's ability to transition from one state to another? What shifts pure potential into matter or back again?

Quantum Physics also offers explanations within the field of physics. What happens within the human body is another ripe terrain for observation, psychology, medicine, and all of the fields that intersect it.

New Science on the nervous system, pioneered by Stephen Porges, also overturns our entire view of how the human nervous system works. His theory, the Polyvagal Theory on the nervous system, suggests that it is the observer, the human being, and one's consciousness that is at the center of what is occurring in the autonomic nervous system. The theory long held and respected in the field of science and allopathic medicine is that there is a stimulus perceived by a human system and, as a result, a response. S - R is the abbreviation for this. What's missing is a link *between* the stimulus and response. The traditional model suggests our response is automatic. A perception by the nervous system that has the power to alter heart rate, blood flow, digestion, and reproduction, and our ability to move or not move has no intermediary. It is purely biological and created by threat. Porges, however, puts us back in the middle and suggests it is our perception of threat that creates this alteration in our biology. The abbreviation looks like this S - O - R, where O is the observer, you. His work is groundbreaking in that it reorganizes the science to put human perception back into the equation. It also suggests that the body, not the mind, is perceiving its environment. So his theory gives the body an intelligence that was removed in our prior understanding of the nervous system and the medicine we have designed to treat it.

Furthermore, our perception is based on prior experiences with safety or danger. This suggests that experience can be held as a memory in the cells, an idea which validates Somatic therapies, and the life-altering experiences we have when memories, including traumatic ones, are addressed and cleared on a cellular level. Porges's work has profound implications for how we practice medicine and implement therapy today.

This morning when I wandered up the road at dawn, I followed the sound of the cicadas. Up into the dry and rocky riverbed, toward the sun. The piñon and ponderosa and juniper were also stretching their limbs into the day. Mine were less sore today, having slept on the floor. The floor, much more solid and firm, always seems to remedy my sore body after a night on a cushy bed. And my 10-year-old, Rafa, was delighted to trade me his camping pad and sleeping bag for a bed.

I felt the drive of the city pace, the fast car, and the fast life pushing me quickly into the hills. Also, the awareness my children were just waking up in the tent, hungry. It took me a while to slow down. And to remember: Oliver's nose is still bleeding. Hard, on and off for a few days now. What am I going to do?

There's a new Golden Yarrow plant in the field just next to the garden on the property where they have allowed us to camp. Yarrow: a plant the midwife uses as an herbal tincture to stop excess bleeding in childbirth. Perhaps I can make a medicine. Tinctures take at least 30 days to make. A flower essence, however, just a day. Golden Yarrow, when prepared as a flower essence, treats extreme sensitivity and re-enforces the protective shield, an energetic boundary that surrounds one's body. If I can find a crystal or ceramic bowl or even a glass, cut the head off of the blossoming flower, place into bowl, cover with pure water, and let it sit today, then at least I'll have an essence to give him. It's worth a try.

It's sitting now, in the strawberry patch, soaking in the sun, the water adjusting to and forming to the vibration of the flower.

It's 8:30 am, and the sun is hot. I do find the children awake in the tent, playing UNO, when I return to the campsite. I push my way a little farther though, through the tall grasses, elder flowers, and shrubs. I wonder what they are called? Farther up the acequia, whose rushing water kept me awake most of the night, I dip myself into a place in the water where it's deep enough to fully submerge my body.

Hello! Hello! Hello!! It's cold. And clear. And pure. So cold and clean and pure.

"It's pure," I will tell them when they ask, "Why do you come here?" Or rather, "Go there?" The wild place so far away from everything. Filled with spiders, mosquitos, overgrown grass, ticks, fleas, biting bugs of all kinds. Too hot in the day and too cold at night. Its buildings and people in disrepair, their properties filled with old cars, tractors, tires, trash. No restaurants, no shops, hospitals, paved roads. Not even a grocery store to buy food. Nothing to do. Why would you possibly want to go there? They wonder.

"Because it's pure," I will say. The medicine is right there, beside us. There's food growing everywhere, even where it looks like there is none. It's between the squash and corn and beans that are planted together on purpose, in the field over there. The lambsquarter, purslane, and dandelion leaves. They fill a bowl like a salad and nourish my being like nothing I can find in the store. Because here, I can show my children how to see. And feel. And really know what is around them—that the weeds are food and medicine. That the bugs are pollinators and an essential piece to why there are flowers. And that before there is fruit, we must have flowers. So our lives depend on all of these things. Here I cannot just tell them, but show them this.

I find them today, washing their clothes in the stream. This is after I told them to be careful, we have nowhere to wash our clothes for a few days!

"Duh, mom," they say, in not such offensive terms, to me.

We have a rocky stream right here to wash them in. They rub their shirts and shorts against the rocks to loosen the dirt, the way we learned in Central America, and dry their clothes on a line suspended from the roof of our tent.

I can show them here that it's ok to be too hot and too cold because that's what's going on outside, all around us. Not like air conditioning or heaters, but connected to what life all around us is experiencing. And in this connection, we are well. Ok. Safe. Not dependent upon unstable systems that are both potentially harmful and keep us enslaved perhaps to work we aren't inspired to do, just to pay the bills.

They can experience it for themselves, feeling safe here, in the wilderness, without a phone, a hospital, or a refrigerator. They see for themselves that when we make trash, we then have to put it somewhere. There is no garbage service here to carry it out, so we must. Therefore, be mindful of what you are using. Our trash will take the place of what once lived here: open space, clean water, clear air. The real things that give life. Source.

The dandelion flowers here are as a big as my fist, and when you blow on them, the white down pulls off the "priests crown" (the name for the disc in the center of the flower) in an umbrella with a full set of spokes, each one with an entire canvas of white down. Then a pole to suspend it in the air and let it float, leisurely to the ground.

So when the boys pick one and blow it for a wish, I tell them it better be a good wish. Not for something they want to buy or obtain. But maybe a feeling they wish to have.

We are in the land here of the Inmortal Root. Also called Wild Cotton, or Antelope horns for its spiked horn-like leaves, it has been used by the Indigenous for generations as medicine. It can decongest the lungs, reduce a fever, alleviate depression, and even assist in childbirth when a woman is having trouble expelling the placenta. It can also be applied topically for skin conditions: rashes, cuts, scrapes, or burns. With just a cup of this plant medicine, made into a decoction, or a tea, you have the power to treat multiple and serious conditions. Not a cough medicine, or an aspirin, or an anti-depressant, or a pill. Just a plant, boiled in water, or steeped in alcohol, taken in your mouth like food or water can heal you. (Peter Holmes, *The Energetics of Western Herbs, Vol. 1, 3rd edition, 1997*)

 Medicine from leaves and flowers (a decoction) - *making a decoction is a lot like making tea, only the plant steeps longer and its medicine is more concentrated. Dried roots must be simmered longer, 20-30 minutes, and fresh leaves or flowers, only 5 to 10. Patience is another necessary ingredient, for letting the plant water cool after boiling is essential to extracting its medicinal properties.*

Approx. 1 to 3 tsp plant, fresh or dried
Approx. 1 to 2 cups cold water
Breath

Place plant/herb in cold water in a saucepan, then place on stove over medium heat. Bring to a boil. Let simmer approx. 20 to 30 minutes. Remove from heat. Let cool, then strain. Drink as a tea, or apply topically on skin condition.

We helped Roslyn, our hostess on the property where we are camping, in her garden yesterday. Getting the weeds out from in between the squash, corn, and beans that are planted together in the field beside the teepee (together because each depends on the other for its healthy growth and development). I had the weeds, lambsquarters, and dandelion today for lunch, rinsed and tossed in some fresh lime and olive oil. Those and the micro-greens from Jordan's grow house just over the hill from Old Gem Farm.

Micro-greens: seeds that sprout down pushing their roots down into a tray of soil while their green life force extends up into a plant. Jordan says that often, after he plants the seeds, he stacks the trays one on top of the other. When they are sprouting, they sometimes push up so hard that a tray can topple over the one above it!! So strong is their impulse upward, toward life. I think we taste this life force in the sprouts. Their vitality literally dances on my tongue when I taste them.

Scientifically speaking, micro-greens are mini-plants. They are seeds planted in trays of soil that, in just seven to 21 days, germinate, sprout, and reach their full size as an edible plant, falling into their own category somewhere between a sprout and a lettuce or salad green. Ecologically speaking, not only are they easier to grow, taking approximately two weeks instead of two months like a head of lettuce, but they also require significantly less space and water to grow. So they are the future, a promising vision for the future of food.

From a nutrition perspective, they are packed with vitamins, minerals, and antioxidants and are 40% more concentrated in nutrients than your basic salad. So, if you are blessed enough to come across some at the farmers market, take them home!! Put them on your salad, in your sandwich, on top of your eggs or pizza. And see for yourself what it feels like to have something dance on your tongue and ignite your body with good energy and life-force. This is the future of food.

"All I can ask is that you tell me whether I can hope to win your love."

"I don't know what to say…give me time to think."

"No. No, I can't!! I need an answer now: You don't have to think about love, you either feel it, or you don't." —Laura Esquivel, *Like Water for Chocolate*

Wild Greens Salad - *undomesticated food holds special power for me. It is original and untamed and therefore has a potency we will not find in our food at the store. Like an apple from a tree that has no owner or twin. It contains minerals from a soil that is not over-taxed and a vibrancy of spirit from a tree that gives at will, not demand. It also may have beneficial gut micro-organisms that help restore and balance an overworked and undernourished digestive system. You can often taste the difference in its ALIVENESS.*

Dandelion, Lambsquaters, Mustard greens, Purslane, micro-greens.

Vision
Lemon, olive oil, salt, dried fruit, wild harvested nuts or seeds.

Wander. Pay attention. Notice edible plants. Harvest. Wash. Separate and keep the younger tender greens. Toss in a bowl with dried cranberries, pine nuts, olive oil, lemon, celery.

"Mom, I feel like a pint of ice cream!" Says Rafa, again. This is day three away from home, the fridge, the freezer. Day three of feeling hungry and not being able to do anything about it. Day Three of having his mother say, "Breathe." And "feel your feet."

Finally today, I thought I'd elaborate on it.

"So, you're hungry. It's hard. I know!! I hear that. And it's just a sensation. You're ok. You're going to be ok."

A little farther down the road, it occurred to me: "Being hungry is a feeling. A feeling we usually respond to with food. But, like all feelings, there are other ways to respond to it. Your breath, for example.

The boys, ages 3, 6, 10, and 13, probably didn't appreciate the example of the nun in the remote town in China who is 97 years old and hasn't eaten in over 10 years. I met her in 2002 on a trip with a group studying Qigong, and I saw with my own eyes just how full and vibrant her face was. How strong her body looked, and how much light was in her eyes. They didn't appreciate that example, but they listened.

"She doesn't eat," they told me and my group, and I now told my children. She lives by the connection of her breath, or simply, on her breath.

It sounds, even to me, like "Orgasmic Birth." They say, it has been said, it has been known to happen, that a woman, once in a while, has an orgasm while giving birth! She actually has an ecstatic, positive bodily sensation as she is pushing the baby down and out of her birth canal. Sounds a bit like an ancient Qigong nun who lives and sustains herself entirely on her breath. But these are the stories that inspire and motivate me. That stoke my curiosity and suggest that things aren't always as they seem. So I pass them along.

It's 1:20 now. Everyone is hungry. Rafa had literally thrown up his one bite of micro-greens, and the boys are sitting quietly, mostly listening to their mom talk about a woman who never ate.

We were clearly all relieved by the beef jerky and two cans of Fresca/Fanta from the gas station 10 minutes down the road.

THE SUBTLETIES OF ADDICTION

Since I was on a roll, I couldn't help but say something about addiction, or, when you REALLY WANT something every day at the same time, like, in this somewhat innocent case, ice cream. You want it so much that it commands your entire focus. It takes your attention out of present time and fastens it to your desire. This is what I call addiction. And this is when it's time to stop, I tell them. Because when you break it, that need and drive to have that "thing," then you find freedom. This is what Freedom feels like. And nothing is more delicious than freedom. I keep my explanation brief.

Except of course falling in love with a girl, or in my case a boy/man. In which case you might even consider exchanging your freedom for that feeling. This is when they finally speak up and officially tell me to just stop talking!

 **Give Me Cream Non-dairy Dessert** - *this frozen treat helps to wean us from our ice cream love/obsession/desire. It is cold, sweet, free from dairy, and alive with natural sugars, minerals, and vitamins.*

1 cup frozen fruit (bananas or peaches or strawberries, or raspberries), blended
1 cup almond/oat/flax/coconut milk
1 to 2 dates to sweeten if desired
Foresight

Mix approximately one cup of fruit with one cup of "milk." Add date to sweeten (optional). Blend until smooth and serve.

I prefer to cut my fruit and vegetables as little as possible. I leave them as whole chunks to bite off with my teeth. They have always tasted better to me like that.

EARTH MEDICINE, A WAY FORWARD

True medicine must have Reverence for all living forms at the heart of it. Chinese Medicine knows this. Ayurveda knows this. Homeopathy knows this. Naturopathic Medicine knows this. Anthroposophic Medicine knows this. Herbal or Plant Medicine and Nutrition or Food Medicine know this. Various forms of bodywork including Massage, Craniosacral therapy,

Polarity therapy, Intuitive Healing, and Spiritual Healing, all know that respect for Planet Earth in its various manifestations is a key factor in how we heal. If we can't put this back at the starting point of medicine, how do we begin to proceed?

The allopathic model of our current philosophy or health care in the United States and other developed countries, however, keeps forgetting (perhaps denying or overlooking) these key elements of relationship and balance between and within living forms. The pharmaceutical industry, while founded on the principle of saving lives, as an institution has an often negative impact on both the earth and our individual bodies. Whether its medicine literally bombs disease out of the body, or the medical waste destroys the water systems it ends up in, the endpoint of its medicine is not balancing or restorative to health.

Earth Medicine, on the other hand, takes the relationships between element—earth, water, fire, air (metal), and ether—and shines light on their importance. What are they? How do they relate? How do they embody or manifest in form? How do they show up, both around us and inside of us? These are the questions that effective practitioners are asking, in all sorts of alternative and complementary fields of medicine, to find healing for their patients and clients. These questions acknowledge the intimate and undeniable relationship between ourselves and the natural world.

The sun was already up this morning when I crept out of the tent. I had crawled deeper into the sleeping bag at dusk when I saw it coming. My head hurt when I simply imagined being awake, and my body still felt the tension of travel, just me alone here with four boys. It wasn't until I imagined *him* kissing me, and my mouth softened into that receptive and joyful place, that I felt the rest of me let go. I even felt my digestion finally kick in, like a gurgling in your belly that lets you know you're hungry now and can begin to receive. I followed that trail of receptivity and willingness back into sleep.

So when I crept out into the early day, I finally felt slower. I could see, with a little more presence now, the cliff of petrified magma we call rocks suspended above our campsite. My need to move, the urgency I brought from the city to just move my body, finally took second place to the ecstasy of just being here.

I walked up the road (in my moccasins) more slowly, noticing my feet on the soft dirt road. Feeling my body a little fuller and more feminine than yesterday. And this time, instead of taking the trail up into the dry riverbed of Carson National Forest, I went straight up a shoulder to a peak where the crows sat. The earth was tender, soft. A cactus, just sprouting in infancy, was also blossoming, and a wildflower volunteered itself nearby. Round river rocks, ponderosa, a circle of piñon, some alive, some dead and dry, crowned this modest peak.

The crows cawed. I listened. Are they afraid of me? Is this a warning cry? Or something else? Sometimes at home, I notice one crow calls to others and they come, filling the branches of a tree in some sort of sacred council. I wonder if I am witness or subject in this council. On dark days, it scares me. On others, I feel that magical merging of past/presence/future they say the crow embodies and wonder if they are helping to usher in my future self.

That's when I remembered to pray. But what is prayer, or how does one even know how to pray? Learn how to pray? Feel that their prayer is real and authentic?

"Growing up I thought God was a woman, and She was the protector of the Natural World."
—**Carly Ball (neighbor on growing up without religion)**

There are as many forms of God as there are individuals, I remember telling Alejandro, the father to my second set of boys. A Latin American Catholic. For him, God was singular, masculine. And punitive. Even in love, there was retribution. And punishment. He, Alejandro, knew the ways of the wild like no one I have ever known. He put deer in the freezer and chickens in the backyard. He kicked off his shoes when the earth was soft and strapped on his boots when work was hard. He could connect to a dog, or a sheep, or a goat across the field with just a look in his eye. And, as a child, he hunted iguanas with a bow-and-arrow for dinner. But for him, God had a singular face that we were all supposed to see in a certain way.

For me, God has many faces. And many names. And can appear in moments like this, far from church, people, and recited prayers. Looking now, from this particular point of view, I am noticing that I feel "God," "Source," "Creation," "Divine," "Ecstatic Union," or simply "Union" most of all when I can feel my body.

So after an exercise of dropping down into the ground (p 212), into my body, I begin my prayer. I have a new practice of calling in angels. Yes, angels. By name. Just as they have done across religions and disciplines for thousands of years: Catholicism, Gnosticism, Christianity, now Medical Intuitives, and Shamanic Healers from native cultures and modern ones. So, while all education and cultural savvy warns me against hokiness, or at least admitting to it, in the Spirit of Healing, I try it out:

"Angel of Harmony. Angel of Grace. Angels of Light." I pause, each time, allowing my words to drift into the time/space beyond me. Giving myself a chance to feel the sensation in my body that comes when I speak these words, call these names, invite this possibility, that there are angels. I feel a relaxation, a surrender, an arrival in present space time that I can't seem to achieve any other way. So it feels real.

Angel of Solidarity. Angel of…. Do I call in Deliverance today? No, she has served me already so completely. She has lifted me up out of that dungeon of doubt and fear. I'll leave her alone today. Instead, I'll call Faith. Angel of Faith. And finally, Angel of Purpose.

This is how I pray, today. Yes, it is intention, like we are taught in diverse forms of Yoga. These are first concepts in my mind. But they are also sensations in my body. Feeling states. And I will modestly suggest, after walking many trails and arriving at numerous dead ends with continued states of contraction and mental agitation, they are also beings of light that come to serve us. Guardian Angels? Ascended Masters? Spirit Guides? Soldiers of God? Elevated ancestors? I don't know! I do know that the state of relaxation and ease I achieve when I speak to them is unique. Their presence, and protection, is experiential, a felt sense.

I finish my prayers with one to each direction, again a practice that has come to us across cultures, disciplines, and spiritual inclinations. Ones that believe there are beings/masters/Archangels/guides that embody the characteristics of each direction and help guide us through the cycles of life symbolized in North, South, East, and West. The teachings are directional, as in the teachings of the Medicine Wheel. I bow now to each group in each direction and find my way down the shoulder of the lomo, back to camp where the boys are just waking up.

I have in my hand a fistful of piñon sap I carefully harvested from the wounds of a tree where I said my prayers. They are like fragrant tears that I burn to remind me that I am not alone. And to carry my prayers into the air. The Holy Mother Piñon, she has me. So my heart and hands are full, and I can meet my boys completely ready to receive.

TOOLS FOR HEALING

The tools for healing with Earth Medicine are many. There is observation and intuition; directing energy with anything from the mind to the hands, needles, or machines that emit currents, food, nutritional supplements, and plant remedies. Other remedies include homeopathic remedies, teas, tinctures, essences, capsules, forms of detoxification, juicing, restoration, sweat baths, saunas, retreats, and rituals. The list of tools we employ under the category of Earth Medicine goes on and on.

In addition, Earth Medicine, as I am defining it, can be offered or administered by a practitioner or, just as importantly, employed by oneself. The question at the center is how do I restore balance? What does it feel like? Look like? What is the impact on my biological chemistry? On my emotional sense of well-being? On my mind, soul, and spirit?

"Do you know the difference between soul and spirit?" I asked my seven-year-old yesterday, when we were in the garden. He was jumping on the trampoline when he started to talk about soul and spirit.

"No," he responded in earnest, now not so sure about what he was saying.

What could I say to him? I think, in a few words, it would go like this: "Spirit projects from the mind and reaches out even farther than the soul. Soul is from the heart and is the intermediary between the Mind, Spirit, and the Body."

Yes, something like this could work, I think.

Feminine Elements of Earth Medicine

"That which comes from Her living body. The plants, the herbs, the touch of a gifted set of hands from a living and breathing human that bring something rich and relevant to our bodies, our beings. Potent, healing touch, laced with the prayer of invisible arcs and circles in which the living, breathing world lives. Not lines, angles, and squares, but round, full shapes. The feminine aspect of our earth beings. These are what lead us back from the land of the lost and into the luminous and hungry world of womanhood, of adulthood." —**Merrill Page**

It rained last night in the desert, and this morning it smells damp and clean.

We're in a canyon now, at the end of a dirt road on a dry riverbed, in a proper house with screen doors, thick walls, a refrigerator, lights, wi-fi. Our camping trip is over, and we've come back to the medicine of "home." Only here, the home is entirely built from the earth of the local landscape. Its walls are thick adobe, which keeps the heat out in the day and the warm in at night. The corners of the building are round and feminine. The exposed beams are artistic and exquisite. The muted colors of the walls are rich, soothing, and match the world that surrounds them. Here, in a home that echoes so beautifully the aesthetic and materials of the desert around it and the natural elements in general, just the feeling of being inside is therapeutic.

But the relief was momentary. Inside these cool, earthy walls I feel separate, sad about what we have lost. Even with all of the bites and scratches on my legs and the boys complaining about theirs, being inside is different. Contained. Predictable. In a word: separate. So in the morning, when I wake up, I go out for a walk.

Walking up into the canyon this morning there is still a buzz of cicadas. A hummingbird, a giant black beetle. Ants. I have to watch more carefully now where I step, as there are cacti sprouting from the damp, soft ground. I'm reminded of those six weeks we spent in Chinandega Nicaragua when Remi was in nursery school, walking down the crowded, semi-paved, broken, and sometimes trepidatious streets. There were holes in the cement, dog poop, puddles. Dirt. Deep, tall drop-offs from the curb into an unpredictable and busy road. Rafa did not at all understand why, with all of the beautiful places in the world, we were here.

"You're here to wake up!" I would tell him. "Get on your toes! Pay attention. Watch where you step." The theme seems to be repeating itself here, again: Watch where you step! There are cacti here begging their way out of the ground and into life, like there are mines, invisible and real on the path ahead. So pay attention.

It's an exercise we do, paying attention when we walk. Feeling into the ground where we step. The more we feel into the ground when we walk, the more we feel. Pretty soon, with all of the feeling of the ground beneath you, you might start to feel like you really belong somewhere. Or don't belong, and then you have a choice to move on. And isn't this at the heart of our deepest longing anyway? To actually belong. To a place... To a person... or In your own Body.

If you start to notice your feet hitting, then touching, then perhaps even unfolding onto the ground beneath you, you may see differently where you are. And when you change the way you see, everything changes.

 **Homemade Handmade Tortillas** - *the earthiness of the corn and the minerals in the calcium in the natural lime used to make traditional corn tortillas have made them something I will always love, despite the controversy around corn and its current safety. They are simple and provide the backdrop for the complexity and spiciness in many Mayan meals. Whether eaten just with salt, with a fresh avocado, or with a divine*

stew of white beans, charred tomatoes, and dried fish, corn tortillas are an essential in a native Mayan kitchen. The experience of making them is also a wonderful way to include children in the kitchen. It provides an activity, a cooking lesson, as well as the sensory stimulation of having their hands in dough. If you have herbs in the garden, pick, rinse, dry, chop, and put them into the batter! Sage, parsley, oregano, thyme, cilantro, dandelion, and chives lace them with green, chlorophyll, sunshine, and vitamins and minerals.

Organic stoneground "masa" - pre-made flour of ground corn and lime
Water
Salt
Joy
Chopped herbs (Sage, parsley, oregano, thyme, cilantro, dandelion, chives…)

Combine approx. 2 cups masa and 1 1/2 cups water in a bowl. Add a pinch of salt. Combine with your hands until mixture is moist and doughy. Not so watery that it sticks on your hands, and not so dry that it crumbles. Make into balls approx. size of a fist. Press in a tortilla press or use wax paper and use a cutting board or your fingers to press into thin pancakes that don't fall apart when you remove paper. Heat skillet over low/med heat and peel gently from wax paper. Place on skillet and cook both sides approx. 2 minutes or until toasty.

Add this salad and you have a meal…

Greek Salad - *this "salad" has all of the elements of a complete meal. I love it for its simplicity and balance, its durability in an extreme climate, and longevity of ingredients on the countertop or in the fridge. It is truly rooted in place, Greece, and whispers of a time when food came directly from the land to home. Feta gives it weight and creaminess to fill you up, and the tomatoes, onions, and lemon are all cleansing and protective, in terms of boosting your immune system.*

Plum tomato
Pink onion
Olives
Feta, crumbled
Stamina
Preserved lemon + olive oil to taste

Slice and toss in bowl with olive oil and a dash of preserved lemon if you have it.

The sun rose strong and bright just after 6 this morning. I traded out my pajama shorts for another pair and wandered outside for a final walk before we go back to California. A walk? A run? A moment for prayer? I walked, pondering my choices. Then I ran when I got to the shade. Slow. Then faster. Straight, then rounding into the curve of a canyoned wall at a turn in the old riverbed. There, between arching bushes, banana yucca, sunflowers, cane cholla cacti, and giant Apache Plume. I dodged and ducked. Stopping occasionally to pick a thorny or spiked seed out of the arch of my sandaled foot. Accelerating, then slowing down, then speeding up again.

Laughing now, I remembered the story of the Indigenous boys who run and run and run, as far as their hearts can manage and their legs will go. They run with each other not in competition for speed or distance. It's not a race (though they call it that). It's an offering. An offering to the Holy Spirits that they believe breathe life into them. It's an offering to their community who is at home, waiting with a feast for when they finally tire and return. And finally, it's an offering to themselves, for them to see what they are made of. Young men at the threshold of manhood racing to see who they are, not to see who they beat, or against whom they win.

But for them to see themselves.

To see and to feel what carries them when they think they can't carry themselves anymore. Each of them knows to offer a word of encouragement to the neighbor running beside him when it gets tough and he doubts that he can keep going.

A word, a look, a hand.

A slowing down to keep pace with your friend, because he, like you, is running to "feed God." And when "God" is fed, we are all better for it. This is what an Indigenous running race is made of, Martin Prechtel reports in his books. Imagine teaching our boys to run like this.

So my run/walk/meditation/memoir, while filled with twists and turns and fallen branches and spikey thorns, carries the breath of the Holy in my memory of how it can be done, and I arrive back to the little adobe home still in the feeling of prayer. I pick some sap off of the bark of the sister piñon trees just up from the back patio and dig a small hole in the dirt to place it in. I start with some dry straw, place the piñon pearls on top, and light a match. In the fire and smoke I send prayers.

I start again by feeling it in my body—dropping where I feel holding. Then open my head, not just my mind, but the aperture, like a camera lens on the top of my skull, and I imagine Spirit coming down from the sky, filling me. I start to pray, and ask, and realize again that first, I must listen. Listen to my thoughts. Listen to the space around me. Listen into the silence.

But flight time is approaching. Chaos is starting to override order. My patience with the boys, who are bouncing around the house, is beginning to seem much less interesting than my authority and ability to delegate our final jobs in closing up the house before we go. I make the mistake of getting up too quickly from my prayer place and transitioning into the tasks. Suddenly I am asking my boys to do things the way I would do them in crunch time: efficiently, orderly, directly. There's nothing round, or curving, or playful about it. We're trying to catch a plane already! And the airport is two hours away.

My eldest is coughing, my third child has sleep—that watery, red, glazed look of sleep, or is it allergies, in his eyes. The second is tripping over his own feet and throwing the pillows off of the bed I just made. The youngest is now screaming for fun and excited about the giant moth on the screen and the beetle that looks like a giant sunflower seed that is broken open, there in his brother's shoe. I am barking orders at them and seeing no results!

When I am done tidying and call for breakfast, guess what!? No one comes. Hunger is less demanding in an environment of order, rush, and command. This is what breaks my heart and helps me soften again into a rounder and fuller place. And only, only when I can achieve this, do they come back to me.

 **Earthy Buckwheat Waffles** - *waffles seem like a shortcut to anyone's heart. These gluten-free, dairy-free, high-protein waffles make them appealing to even the most modern adaptive eater and are ideal for breakfast when you are hungry or want to stay grounded. If you have buckwheat in the cupboard, it's fun to know how to use it.*

Heat waffle iron then combine

1 cup buckwheat flour
1 cup gluten-free flour
1 tsp baking soda
1 tsp baking powder
1 tsp sugar of choice
1/4 tsp salt

Combine and stir until well mixed

3 eggs
1 flax egg (recipe below)
1 cup rice/flax milk
Love
1/2 cup sunflower oil

One flax egg is made by combining 1 tbsp ground flaxseed with 3 tbsp of water. Combine in a small bowl and stir to blend. Let sit approximately 10 to 15 minutes until gelatinous. For 2 eggs, double the recipe.

Combine and whisk until well blended. Fold the wet ingredients into the dry ones and blend until smooth. Spray waffle iron with non-stick coconut oil or olive oil. Pour in correct amount. Close and cook until done. Serve with butter and maple syrup if desired. Or freeze. This recipe should leave you with leftovers, and these are an easy go-to snack.

THE NEW MAPS OF MEDICINE

The other side of Earth Medicine, equally essential, potent, and real, is Energy Medicine. Energy Medicine, a term embraced and popularized by a newer voice in the field, Donna Eden, is as enduring and old as Earth Medicine. It works from the premise that before we are matter, we are energy. We are subtle bodies whose energy steps down through invisible layers into a physical construct we live as our bodies. The subtle bodies in its many layers have been perceived and recorded across the globe and its diverse cultures for as long as we can imagine. The systems of healing born of these maps still persevere today: Chinese Medicine, Yoga and Tantric Healing, Anthroposophic Medicine, Polarity therapy, Qigong Healing Touch, and Therapeutic Touch are examples of this.

The different systems have different maps, layers, and entry points. Daniel Andreev, a twentieth century Russian scholar, whose work has ignited and deepened our global understanding of Spiritual hierarchy and maps of the energy body, proposes that these differences perceived across cultures and timeframes are a result of the many, many layers and energy points of the subtle body.[1] Still, within the disparate understandings, there is overlap, and scientists marvel at the similarity between the meridian maps used in Acupuncture and the tattooed points on a body preserved in the snow some 5,300 years on Otzi, the Iceman. This is a corpse of a Neolithic man that was finally found in the Alps between Austria and Italy in 1991. He has points tattooed on his body that mirror our maps in treatment with the five element theory in Acupuncture.

Moving from the outside in, or stepping down, from the invisible realms into the organs, the most densely concentrated manifestation of matter, there are numerous Energy Fields, Energy Warehouses, Chakras, Meridians, and Points along the Meridians that can be treated with the tools of Energy Medicine. They can be treated through electromagnetic currents using needles, or a biofeedback machine, and they can be treated using the directed intention of the mind, conscious awareness, or the hands with the intention of a practitioner that reflects an awareness of these energy maps.

The tools of healing are intended to open blockages in the energy field (or diverse fields) to allow the body's energy to flow and fill itself. On its own, the body has a capacity to run light currents of its soul/spiritual self through pathways to restore health, vibrancy, and radiance—not only on a physical level, but a spiritual one as well.

"Mom, can I buy something?" Rafa asks.

We have just arrived at the airport in Albuquerque.

"Just some mints?" Rafa says.

At the mention of the word mints, I know he's joking. Phew. For some reason they associate mints with a harmless little treat they can buy at the store. I, however, associate mints with an overwhelming scent or taste that disarms the homeopathic remedies which I give them (for wounds, stings, rashes, colds, earaches, fevers, emotional outbursts, sleeplessness, stings, burning when they pee, diarrhea, etc.). Homeopathy is my go-to for all first-aid remedies and beyond. So the mention of mints as a harmless little candy alarms me. Plus, mints have an overwhelming effect on the other more subtle notes expressing in between the flavor of mint. So mint is not as harmless as it seems. I know he's joking, sort of, but still my body seizes up with the thought of it. Also, he is asking if he can have his very own box of mints to hide and eat in secret as he'd like.

This time, instead of a heated and defiant "No!", instead of a wordy and mental explanation that goes something like this: "It's about your not having something separate and unique from the store that your brothers don't have. Everyone thinks mints are ok, but the flavor and essence are so domineering and override everything else, including the more subtle things that are here to sense and feel, and then your sugar ball remedies (the Homeopathy) I give you." (Yes, mint is clearly my scapegoat here for all that dominates our more subtle perception.) Instead of all that, which he has already heard four times over the past week, I just look at him.

"Kidding," he says.

"Good," I reply. And we make our way to the security line.

"Do not risk injuring what is important for the sake of what is not important." —I Ching

Once on the airplane come the other requests: "Mom. Can I have a Coke? A Sprite? A ginger ale?" Then I hear Oliver telling the man next to him that a world without popcorn is not even worth living in. What!?!? I never knew he felt that way!

"Mom, can I please get a popcorn? I can do it with my own money," he says to me. He's 13, it's only popcorn, I hear myself say to myself. And, knowing I am being witnessed by the man sitting next to him, I find grace. But the answer is "No." And the reason: group mind.

"We are in group mind just a little longer," I say to him.

It has been a week of wrestling down the demons of our individualistic inclinations. All of the single bottled drinks I didn't let them buy, the candy, the mints. All of my "Nos!" to the "Can I just have...?!" have yielded me my own little group of ants. Boys who are now together, working as a group, inclusively, toward the ends of being fed and sheltered. Working as a whole, with the awareness that only when *all* are fed are we truly taken care of.

I saw it tonight, when we were finally home, and Rafa said "No thanks" to the bowl of ice cream I served him. Um, what? No! No? NO!?!?!?! Rafa doesn't want ice cream? And he wasn't charged about it, or mocking, or defiant. It was just a simple no thank you. He was more engaged in something else he was doing and didn't want the ice cream. My world stopped when I heard this.

He seemed so relaxed to me. So at ease with himself and whatever he was doing to nest back into home. He seemed to just be ok with being here. Home. Feeling and seeing and smelling and touching whatever it was he hadn't seen or felt or touched this past week in New Mexico. Yes, there was the possibility of watching TV, which certainly engaged his mind, but when I asked him, directly, "Rafa, you don't want ice cream? Why?" He replied, again, without any charge or excitement, "I don't feel like it." This is the freedom I have been pushing toward. And now, we have arrived!

FINDING BALANCE IN THE ELEMENTS

When we finally unplug from dominant patterns, whether its single serve drinks, eating mints, or working as individuals as opposed to a collective, we start to notice the more subtle elements of life. Each one has a specific and relevant expression which is essential to the balance of the whole. And it is in these elements that our true freedom resides. They, once freely given, are the backdrop of everything we truly need: the earth, the water, the fire, the space of sky or ether. They are where we have come from, and where we must go if balance is to be restored to Modern Medicine.

Again, it is the natural elements, water, fire, wood, air and ether, metal, and earth that serve as the organizing principles in some of these diverse forms of Energy Medicine, including Chinese Medicine, Qigong, Ayurveda, Polarity therapy, and Chakra healing employed in Therapeutic Touch and Tantric Yoga. The elements and their attributes stretch out into the most subtle realms of our experiences, then step down into the most physical ones. Through them, we are able to look at the vibrational aspects of our physical systems.

What are the colors, smells, sounds, seasons, and grains associated with this element?

What are the virtues, the thought patterns, the emotions, and the physical organs connected to this element?

Both Chinese Medicine and Ayurveda, ancient systems of medicine that have endured centuries of trial and error, trace these connections from the elements in Nature as we experience them on our Planet, through the Spirit self of an individual, down into the gross anatomy of the body, and then offer up techniques and strategies for resolving real illnesses. These are systems, some 2,000 years old, which continue to be used today, even with quantitative science and the modern world as our backdrop.

In addition to connecting the planet to the multiple levels of our beings, including spirit, mind, emotions, and the body, these disparate forms of healing move in circles and spirals. We see it both in the process of healing and in the gestures used to heal. To clear stagnant energy in a point, a Hopi healer from a tribe will move his or her hands in a circular motion over a client's body, both in clockwise and counterclockwise directions. To open chakras that are blocked, a practitioner will spiral energy clockwise and counterclockwise over the area on a body that corresponds to that chakra. To prepare for practice and healing, a Qigong healer from China will circle energy over his navel in both directions, clockwise and counterclockwise.

The fact that circular patterns hold immense potency for transformation is exhibited daily by how energy moves on the earth, in tornadoes, in wind currents that spiral, or in how fire bursts up from the circular mouth of a volcano to transform the landscape and climate around it. Sometimes, even gardens are planted in spirals.

Because the movement is round, I will call it feminine. These concepts and techniques point the way for how we can fold feminine elements into the effective, linear and what I call masculine methods used in medicine today.

The boys were up early with me the next day. Seeing there would be no space for silent, contemplative time, and feeling more at ease now with slipping away in the morning, I put on my red campsite sweatpants and moccasins and slipped out the front door to walk.

But today it felt less like driving my body into motion. Less about moving to exercise or alleviate some agitation and need to move, and more about the joy of being outside. The air here in Northern California is heavier with moisture than the air of the desert. A little thicker with the multiple expressions of blooming flowers and vines. A little bit newer, now with our nervous systems settled.

I felt so joyful being outside that I even remembered to say hello to the growing things as I walked past: the Wisteria, Morning Glory, Dogwood, Rosemary, Giant Redwood tree… And look at the plum!! Fruit dripping now, ripe and ready. I hadn't noticed that tree before. The neighbor's gardens? One has plants intertwined and holding each other up, another has a radiant succulent that is full and reaching from its pot into the big sky. I had never seen these, like this, before.

I walked, in my simple, perhaps succulent delight. Then ran. Slow, fast, gently, until I walked again. Until finally back home where I also found the boys at ease in their freedom from me, playing like boys play, without the lines or limitations of their mother.

"You guys! The plums are ripe!" I call to them. "You can come get them and make jam."

They all lit up at the possibility, and then we were there, outside beneath a plum tree a few blocks from our house, all together. I left them picking plums, one up in the tree, and the others below catching the fruit he tossed down. I came home to write, somewhat mystified by the simple and easeful miracles of how we live. Boys here in the suburbs of San Francisco who aren't on a phone or iPad or inside, eating food, or even reading a book, but outside, excited by the prospect and privilege of harvesting a tree. And the tree, relieved to be giving her fruits.

"Mother, it's good to feel your breath again." —**Martin Prechtel**

The wrestling and insistence upon doing things just this way feels rewarded. The reward is not "living right" or "reducing our trash" or "decreasing our waste" or "lightening our footprint." It's something more personal, more rich. It's a feeling of being connected. Being together. Being ok with depending on each other as we move along in space/time/life. Of listening to each other and tracking each other as we move, so we can offer a hand when needed. So we can have experiences that are hard and sometimes scary or uncomfortable, but then get to the other side with a true sense of connection and achievement. This is when I see the brightest sparkle in their eyes and feel the most light and joy from their hearts…when they've actually done something hard. Something that required presence and courage. Like getting up a slippery ledge of a desert canyon mined with thorny cacti and sharp, spikey seeds. Or walking barefoot across large river stones in a fast, strong current of water. These exercises get us into our bodies and balance our brains in ways that science is just looking to understand and quantify. These are real experiences with a teacher named Mother Earth who has no equivalent. The dangers here are different from the dangers and challenges of the mind. The rewards are different, too. And so rich.

 **Cinnamon Plum Breakfast Dessert** - *because we find plums in such abundance all over the neighborhood, being under-appreciated and sometimes scorned for the cleanup they require when they drop their uneaten fruit, we want to rescue them. To savor their unique tartness and unharnessed mineral power. So we make these. It is a great way to "do" dessert.*

5 to 7 plums
1 tsp cinnamon
1/4 cup maple syrup
1/4 lemon
Elderberry (optional)
Connection
Something creamy on top

Combine in saucepan over the stove. Let simmer approximately 30 minutes over low to medium heat or until tender. Serve in bowl with vanilla "nice" cream, yogurt, or flax/rice milk.

Later, we harvested the garden, and then I sent the boys to the store, both giving them something to do and postponing my return to the indentured life of purchasing food at the grocery store.

In the desert, where earth and plants, trees and water are the source of visual interest and attention, it's easier to see the garbage. Each plastic bag that wraps our tortillas, or bread, or hamburger meat…even the earthy, hippie food (like figs and dates, yogurt, organic crackers, or hummus) would ultimately end up on the landscape. It's easier there, in the desert, to make the connection for myself and for my children. Not because we want to limit ourselves or feel guilty. But because we are connected. We cherish the opportunity to pick a fruit from a tree or a weed from the garden that we can then even eat! In the end, it is not just fresh and fun, but more fulfilling and really, the way.

So when I call Rafa over to the Co-op where I am keeping the garden, and he doesn't really feel like picking blueberries (they are too small! he says), I have to find a way to connect him to *him*. Of course, the possibility of blueberries with yogurt and honey helps. As does the suggestion that we won't be buying fruit at the store a block away. And it helps him to know his friends are away, and there is no one nearby he can run off to play with. I am able to pull a few minutes of picking out of those fingers, enough to fill a basket, and exercise the nimbleness in his fingers and connections in his brain.

I also can't resist telling him that this can be a substitute for the sit-ups his father is insisting upon. If he squats down and pulls his belly button to his spine, as they say in Pilates, or just engages his core muscles, as they say at the gym or in Yoga class, he'll get his tummy workout. It can be so easy.

URBAN MEDICINE

What can we do for medicine, now that we are home in our Urban Suburb and away from the wilds? Alexei's back is covered in an "Alien" rash, his brother so aptly named it, and it's not going away!!!

The small puss-ey, are they welts or bites? are up into the base of his skull, into his hair. And the more superficial bumps that look like an allergic reaction to laundry soap, or something, have spread all over his back.

Water seems to irritate it. And it looks like it needs something dry, not ointment. When I remember to think in terms of plant remedies, basil keeps coming to mind. I don't know why, but the idea, basil, just won't leave me alone.

It seems too simple. Though I know the Mayan's and Indian's consider it a sacred plant. And the herbalists claim it's anti-inflammatory, anti-parasitic, calming.

Then, there are the Italians…for them, basil is a legend in the kitchen.

I took it once for an incurable case of dysentery when I lived in the Western Highlands of Guatemala in the 1990s. I drank it as a tea, and it worked right away. I was shocked. Amazed. Humbled. Then I forgot. It seemed too mild to be the real remedy. So I doubted it. But there was no denying the relationship between my drinking the tea on an empty stomach three times that day and the diarrhea stopping.

Basil.

So I asked the boys to get me basil, with the toilet paper, when they went to Safeway.

They came back with a little basil plant, packaged with its roots. They apologized for not being able to find a bundle of basil without roots!!

"Good. It's ok! Thank you," I said, and wondered and hoped that this basil, with its roots, might carry the spirit of the plant.

So we put it to boil, a handful of the plant in a cup of water. Simmered it for approximately two minutes. Turned off the stove. Let it steep for 10 to 20 minutes. Let it cool, and washed Alexei's back. He screamed that it stung!!! Um, what!?!? Is it that strong?? The basil water stung his "Alien" back.

Basil water stings? I couldn't believe it. We patted it dry and woke up the next morning to a back, that after six days of getting worse, looked like it was improving. Amazing. Simple. Easy. Clean. Harmless. Connected. The rash, within two days of doing this, went away entirely. Even the welts in his hair along the occiput in the back cleared up right away.

 Basil Bath - *making medicine from familiar plants starts with a beginner's mind. It requires intuition, deep listening, and a commitment to remembering that the edibles and plants we live with everyday are capable of bringing magic and healing to us in simple ways.*

One bunch of basil
2 to 3 cups water
Mystery

Rinse and place bunch of basil in a small heavy stock pan with water, over medium heat on stove. Cook for 2 minutes on medium heat. Lower heat and simmer 3 to 5 more minutes. Turn off heat. Let cool, and apply water to rash.

"There is something the poison oak plant wants to communicate to you," one witchy practitioner of plant medicine told me, when I came begging for help. "This is how plants work. They choose us to communicate with. The poison oak, in this case relentless, is wanting to tell you something."

"But what, what is it?" I ask, my innocent inquiry begging a thorough and complete answer.

"Poison Oak, as I know it, embodies the aggressive energy of the male. It speaks to boundaries and how we hold them, or don't," she told me. She went on to point out how poison oak lines the rivers, the oak trees, and the trails where I walk in California, and perhaps here serves as a protection to the wild, to keep us from treading on the sacred, untouched ground.

For a moment, I shifted out of my victim psychology, where I feel like I am under attack from a plant who is "after me," and into a plant-centric psychology where I catch a glimpse beyond how this plant serves me. What if it is acting in service to the wildscape of Mother Nature, protecting her from our unconscious encroachment upon her virgin body?

Still, there are pieces I have yet to comprehend. About why this uncontrollable allergy started just before I gave birth to Remi. And how it might be related to my hormonal profile or nutritional balance on a cellular level, as more and more of my building blocks are offered up to construct the body of a baby. Was there a relationship between Remi not coming out on a rushing river of amniotic fluid and my crazy full-body case of poison oak just before he was born?

Or, how the outbreaks on my body may be connected to the deeper fires inside of me that burn through my skin and come often in moments of passionate conflict, internal and interactive, with those who share my home?

Some of these pieces I will never come to comprehend. But I have noticed that when I bring my attention to nurturing the deeper, cooling waters I call feminine energy, and stay on trail and in relationship to protection, I have fewer outbreaks. This question *How do I protect myself?* begins to capture my imagination for years to come.

MAKING MEDICINE IN YOUR KITCHEN

When I look up "basil" in Peter Holmes' *The Energetics of Western Herbs*, I find it in the section of herbs that promote expectoration and resolve phlegm and colds. It is for lung conditions. It can also settle the stomach and aid with digestion, harmonize menstruation, and even restore nerves. It promotes clear thinking and relieves fatigue and depression.

The hopes for relief are many and run the gamut. But I don't see anything about parasites (as perhaps Alexei had in his skin) or skin conditions like poison oak.

Then, approaching the altar for prayer, I remember: in Chinese Medicine, treating the lungs *is* treating the skin. They are intimately connected and influence each other directly. We breathe through our skin as we do our lungs. And in Ayurveda, digestion and stomach wellness are at the root of being well. If your digestive fire is strong, the rest of your systems can benefit from your nutrition and run well as a result. Looking from these different angles, even taking the basil topically has the potential impact of treating the multiple systems.

Then, there's just fact and observation: he is better.

I am humbled, over and over, by the simplicity of it.

I am reminded of my work in Guatemala in 1998 with the Cachiquel Village of the Mayan people...where I was "teaching" or, more accurately, "remembering" with them that, if we can just begin to notice what is growing around us and living with us, we can begin to reclaim so many things: our surroundings, our health, our bodies, our freedom.

Just start by noticing, who else is here?

Ask yourself their names.

Inquire about how they are.

Wonder what their purpose is.

With just these basic observations and questions, we can begin to transform in miraculous ways. Through our curiosity and our connection. Those in and of themselves are the real treasures. But then, beyond that, we begin to discover Earth Medicine. The possibility of healing a wound from a clump of basil in the garden or a weed called mallow at the side of the road and bike path. Or the promise of treating a cold with the thyme and rosemary growing outside the front door. Or staving off a flu, not with a vaccine from the pharmacy, but with a syrup from the elderberry growing over the hill. There is a syrup there, at your local health food store, if you don't have it in you to make one.

This way, delightful unto itself, is also a path to freedom. Freedom from the things that drive you far from your home. The many needs we have that keep us dependent on unsustainable systems. From medicine to food, transportation to shelter. All of these things we think we depend on can shift with some basic shifts in perception. They start with simply connecting with what is right there at hand.

Then, there is the freedom of experiencing things you never imagined if you just stop worrying about being sick and know that true medicine is there, already growing as weeds and volunteers in the ground. What does it look like to harvest and support this paradigm for medicine? What does it feel like? How is it done?

Start by making more of the things you need yourself! This reduces your dependency, reduces waste, and reduces unnecessary ingredients and chemical waste in your home

Mouthwash

1 cup water
1 tbsp hydrogen peroxide

Combine in a glass and leave by the sink to gargle with occasionally over course of two to three days. No mint!! And no extra garbage of mouthwash bottles you have to buy to replace.

Household Cleaner

Empty spray bottle
Some 20 drops of lavender essential oil
Some 5 tbsp hydrogen peroxide
Approx. 30 to 40 drops grapefruit seed extract
Water to fill bottle

Combine all ingredients in spray bottle and use leisurely throughout house (walls, floors, countertops, toilet seats, sinks, surfaces) knowing it is safe and non-toxic and doesn't require you to purchase a plastic bottle every time you run out. Mine seems to last at least a month.

Toothpaste (powder)

1 tbsp activated charcoal
1 tbsp Calcium Bentonite clay
1 tbsp baking powder

Combine in dish and place next to sink to use as you would toothpaste. Again, no mint (which is believed to interrupt homeopathic remedies) and no extra toothpaste tubes in your garbage!! Plus, clean teeth!

Not everyone lives in proximity to plants, whether by choice or not. So many people can't imagine this way. Still, there are ways to support Earth and Plant Medicine with small choices: an herbal tea instead of an Alka-Seltzer. A flower essence instead of an aspirin. A ginger tea or syrup instead of a cough medicine. A homeopathic remedy instead of a Motrin or fever reducer.

Garlic-Mullein ear drops instead of antibiotics. Fruit for snacks instead of chips or cookies. Bodywork instead of back surgery. Acupuncture instead of a visit to the doctor.

The ways are so numerous, and the possibilities abound when you simply start to consider them options. Even insurance companies are redesigning themselves to support healthy life-giving choices, instead of trying to catch up with disease after it's rooted deeply inside of us. These are the ways into our future.

Protect Me Green Apple Parsley Dressing - *parsley is not only refreshing and packed with trace minerals, it also helps fight pathogens to keep you well and is centering. Plus, it never gives up. Even when all of the other plants in my garden have dried up or faded away, parsley perseveres. It's easy to grow, inexpensive to purchase, and lasts weeks in the fridge. A jar of this dressing can be made and used for days on salads, cooked vegetables, pastas and grains, eggs, or by the spoonful by you, your children, or even babies starting on first food.*

1 green apple (rinsed and cubed)
1 bunch parsley (washed. Cut back stems)
1/2 cup olive oil
2 tbsp water
1 tsp apple cider vinegar
1/2 lemon or lime (juiced)
1 pinch salt
1 pinch cayenne
Deep Vision

Combine ingredients in blender and blend until smooth and creamy. You may need to add a splash more liquid of choice (water, oil, vinegar, or lemon) and pause blender to push down with a pastry spatula, then re-blend until smooth and creamy. Smother on eggs, pasta, tortillas, toast, use as a salad dressing or a salsa on a taco.

The big boys left last night with their dad. So this morning, I am bound to the house, just two littles sleeping upstairs. It takes all of my discipline to not divert my quiet time into laundry, folding, dishes, sweeping, lists, communications, and to simply sit in prayer instead.

There is a little table next to the stove in the kitchen where I sit. The Altar. I have a cupboard where I keep the piñon sap and an old ceramic bowl where I crinkle store receipts to burn the piñon. I keep my collection of other found things in the cupboard: crystals, a sage stick, shells, rocks, feathers, notes. It is modest. Homemade. Storied. The way an altar should be, storied with one's own memories. I kneel there. Engage my tummy, and reach my hands to the sky. I soften my face and breathe.

What is it that is so big about breathing? If you have spent as much time as I have short of breath and anxious, you don't have this question. (Kinda like the conversation about constipation. If you've never been there, you can't understand why someone else is talking about it.) Breathing is just this way. If you lose that deep, rich connection to taking air in and letting it out, you know just how Holy breath is. Not just the relief of having your body animated by this freely given substance we call air, but by the nourishment of it, too. Your breath nourishes you. Your entire system. All of it. It oxygenates your lungs, brain, musculoskeletal system. It regulates your nervous system and helps circulate your blood. It helps remove waste from your body and nourish your skin. It helps distribute hormones, keep your body warm or cool, and balance all things regulated by the endocrine system. All of these bodily functions depend on your breath.

But also, it is your most intimate exchange with everything around you. Your taking breath in and breathing breath out keeps you in deep, bodily relationship with all of life.

I used to wonder why nobody made a bigger deal out of the fact that what we breathe out, the plants breathe in. And their lives depend upon it. Vice versa, what they exhale is what we inhale. And our lives depend upon it. How is this not one of the most miraculous facts of existence? How is it not the cornerstone of every environmentalists' movement? How does it get reduced to a dry scientific fact and one piece of a block in a science classroom? How does it get lost in a lesson and buried under other theories we call important and later dismiss as incorrect? I don't get it.

So I breathe, and feel my breath so deep today. I can even bring it down into my belly and fill that empty space in my womb.

Kneeling at the foot of an old cupboard filled with sap and seeds, I feel the gift of the Southern shield, and its role in how we embody.

Multi Mineral Supplement in your water - I add a few droppers-full of a liquid multi-minerals supplement to our five-gallon jugs of water. It loads our filtered water with the trace minerals we are supposed to be getting in water, fruits, and vegetables. They act as co-enzymes in multiple biological processes in our bodies, helping to regulate the nervous system, grow healthy hair, bones, and teeth, and regulate body temperature and thyroid function, just to name a few.

I wanted to see where beauty comes from
without you in the world, hauling my heart
across sixty acres of northeast meadow,
my pockets filling with flowers.
Then I remembered,
it's you I miss in the brightness
and body of every living name:
rattlebox, yarrow, wild vetch.
You are the green wonder of June,
root and quasar, the thirst for salt.
When I finally understand that people fail
at love, what is left but cinquefoil, thistle,
the paper wings of the dragonfly
aeroplaning the soul with a sudden blue hilarity?
If I get the story right, desire is continuous,
equatorial. There is still so much
I want to know: what you believe
can never be removed from us,
what you dreamed on Walnut Street
in the unanswerable dark of your childhood,
learning pleasure on your own.
Tell me our story: are we impetuous,
are we kind to each other, do we surrender
to what the mind cannot think past?
Where is the evidence I will learn
to be good at loving?

EARTH MEDICINE

The black dog orbits the horseshoe pond
for treefrogs in their plangent emergencies.
There are violet hills,
there is the covenant of duskbirds.
The moon comes over the mountain
like a big peach, and I want to tell you
what I couldn't say the night we rushed
North, how I love the seriousness of your fingers
and the way you go into yourself,
calling my half-name like a secret.
I stand between taproot and treespire.
Here is the compass rose
to help me live through this.
Here are twelve ways of knowing
what blooms even in the blindness
of such longing. Yellow oxeye,
viper's bugloss with its set of pink arms
pleading do not forget me.
We hunger for eloquence.
We measure the isopleths.
I am visiting my life with reckless plenitude.
The air is fragrant with tiny strawberries.
Fireflies turn on their electric wills:
an effulgence. Let me come back
whole, let me remember how to touch you
before it is too late.
~Stacie Cassarino

CHAPTER FIVE

EN EL OCÉANO DE LA INCERTIDUMBRE

IN THE OCEAN OF UNCERTAINTY

The Western Shield

Adolescence

FALL

Fall is easily described as a turning point and is embodied by the simple gesture of a tree dropping its leaves. With winter coming, it has to let go of the ecstatic expression of a leaf and pull its energy down and in. So, too, is the way of the body. Having to let go a little of the laughter, joy, and full engagement that is requested by summer, and then drop into a more internal space that winter begs for. This is the cycle of life, inside and out. It is in respecting and following the gesture of this cycle, its highs and lows and in-betweens, that we maintain our emotional balance and alignment through the seasons of our lives. Ignoring these cycles is what eventually causes depression, disconnection, and mis-alignment, not only with the earth and her ecology, but also with our own. In the dark cave of the Western shield, we are asked to go inward to discern our true gifts.

THE ELEMENTS AS TEACHERS

The final stop on the Medicine Wheel, for the sake of this story, is the West. Here in the Western shield we enter the elemental teachings of earth. At home in the earth element, we are fed by the true nature of who we are and the hard work required to discover, cultivate, and protect that.

EARTH

Earth is the body. Earth is the planet that holds us, feeds us, nurtures us through life. It is the structure, or framework, that allows the rest to unfold in divine timing and choreography. Earth Medicine is the abundance of a fall harvest where we embrace the fruit of the seeds we planted seasons ago. Earth, as the true embodiment of the physical world, also prepares us for the reality of fall and winter, when light fades and the reality of letting go into the inevitable death of winter begins to show its face.

There's something not so soft here. About anything. In Montana, the sky is open. And blue. But there's something edgy in that celestial blue. Or maybe it's the sharpness of the peaks…the naked, treeless, metal grey peaks that cut into the sky and remind me of the blade of a knife.

I felt it this morning, finding my way down to the river for a dip. The rocks weren't so round and form fitting as the round river rocks of New Mexico. They were angled and sharp. Even angry? Feeling the bite of the water, too, reminded me that winter here is hard. Just cold and hard, and perhaps doesn't allow for that softness that other places have the privilege of embodying.

I stripped off my shoes though. They were already wet from slipping down off of a fallen tree into the river, as were my jeans and the soft cashmere sweater that were supposed to be warm enough for an August morning. I was actually warmer with the air touching up against my skin and feeling the dirt and mud under my feet. And then, with the sun rising a little higher over the eastern peak, I dipped myself down into the hole where the water fell hard through a natural damn of branches and rocks. Wow. Wow. Wow. *Remember the fire inside*, I reminded myself as my feet, fingers, and face ached against the running water. Relax into it. Breathe. Still, I wondered: Am I safe? Is it too cold? And, just to be sure, do I still know where I am?

I looked up from this crevasse, two slopes of rock that meet where the river runs up and out into the pines and wildflowers, to see if I recognized where I am. And there at my own edge, I stepped to the side of the river to orient myself in a place I could still recognize as familiar, even as my body explored a new limit of cold.

Sinking down into the cold-running stream, the run-off from the winter snow, is my newest form of therapy. It wakes me up. It makes me feel alive. And today, sitting into a hole just big enough for me to lean back into and relax my head with my body down underneath the water, I feel the amazing encounter that my own system of stress makes with the freezing cold water.

So, it's like training. Yes, Cryotherapy is a form of athletic training where your deepest sense of connection to your own strength and power must rise to meet an external demand. The intensity of what's touching you on the outside is so extreme, so real, so damn cold, that you must draw from a source deep within, where it's hot and clear and confident, in order to survive it.

And that's where the smile comes from, as I lay my body down into a crib of rocks and broken branches. That touching into an internal place that is strong and clear enough to meet the purity and strength of cold on the outside. That ability to meet stress with aplomb and composure. For me, that's what's happening here, beyond my joy of letting go down into the pure water of the Gallatin River. Inside of my privilege of merging myself with a stream that has given itself into the deepest winter, winter in Montana, and then been born again to run so freely here in this form called summer stream. It gives me the experience of re-birth. Of wildness. Of excitement.

"You are the Beloved." —Morgan Day Cecil

I come again and again, day after day, to drop into the hands of these waters. To give myself, over and over, to this cold. Each time it asks me to let go more into trust. Trusting myself, that I have just what I need to meet this extreme situation. Trusting the water to hold me. Trusting grace, that I am safe and will not lose focus, direction, a sense of where I am, or how to find my way home again.

Each time I let go I see something new. Yes, as my 15-year-old nephew says of his experience in the frigid waters, "My arms feel like new!" His tired, athletic, over-worked lacrosse arms feel reborn after a dip in this river. Mine too. All of my body feels alive, new, and awake. But beyond my body, each time I get out, I also see something new in the landscape around me. A flower I didn't notice before. A tree. A shape. A sound. Something that lives there, in the landscape around me, that I had overlooked or not seen before. So my eyes are new too, as is my entire ability to perceive.

This, and of course the motivation of taking years off of my life with my new form of wilderness Cryotherapy, is what motivates me. The way it makes me feel my body and, then, want to eat less. The way I see that butter weight melt off of my butt. Yes, that: the body toning and weight-loss factor, the factor that most motivates my boys to get into the cold water with me. They think perhaps they'll emerge with a six pack without the hours of sit-ups or sweaty physical exertion. That's the inspiration for my 10- and 13-year-olds!

There's a sign outside of the Pilates studio in downtown Larkspur which says: "I really regret that workout, said no one, -ever." Here it is again: "I really regret that dip in the cold stream, said no one, -ever."

Today, my mother came to the stream with me. She watched as I peeled away my clothes and sank myself into the running stream. She photographed me as I smiled in true delight of that extreme, but safe, sensation. Yes, she called me a "nut," but I laughed. And her husband, when he teased me for choosing my healthy ways, was also met with a new sense of ease I have inside me.

"You love to tease me!!" I say to him. "And I thank you! Because at 44, I finally know who I am. And all of your teasing has forced me to look inside and see for myself the motivations for my behaviors."

He can't help but interject, "You already know who you are at 44!? I am 80 next year and still figuring it out." This clearly is not the case, I think to myself, sizing up his life of so many accomplishments and the circle of beloveds around him.

"There are many arrival points," I say to him. And continue on: "But I just want you to know, Johnny, that we are motivated by the same thing. Freedom. I, like you, act and make choices to secure my own freedom. It is the same."

He smiles, and I see the sparkle light his eyes. It's early in the morning, and there's really no need to talk. But this, for me, is an arrival point. This place of non-charge. A place of confidence and ease, where I have taken what for so many years felt like criticism and agents of self-doubt and spoken so directly to them. No, no, no! I will not accept this angle/perspective/pigeonhole. Yes, yes, yes! I will live like I want to live. I agree with that. And still, I will ask, What is the long view? And what really feels good, not just for me, but in the long run, for all of us?

 **Make Me Happy Fruit Bowl** – *breakfast. Why is it so hard for me? Yes, I do love the sensation of emptiness and the deeper awareness it brings. I have learned to treasure my sensitivity, and I hope you will too. So, in the morning when the light is most divine, I am sensitive. Do I want/need something hot? Or cold? Light? Or heavy? Sweet? Salty? Savory? On days when a warm tortilla, my usual heart's desire, seems habitual and misaligned, I look for the fruit of the season. And if my internal fire burns bright enough, I can add cold belly-building (for its probiotics and good fat) yogurt and seeds or grains.*

Late summer cherries or nectarines or peaches in a bowl with plain or Greek yogurt, raisins, and oat/rice milk.
Love
Raw quick oats (add if you're young or hungry)

Combine in a bowl, bow your head in awe, and eat.

The *I Ching* is again, a reservoir of wisdom, just the right nourishment for fall.

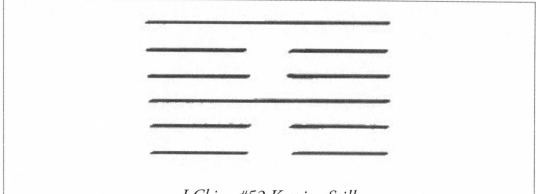

I Ching #52 Keeping Still

Mountain over Mountain is an image for stability. Safety. Groundedness. It offers up mountain as the Earth embodiment for these energetic qualities. A possibility for one who is energetically sensitive, to imagine how to stand strong and clear in an Earthy way, without compromising their sensitivity. With Keeping Still one is reminded of the two-fold nature of coming to an end of a movement or an era. The end of one phase is always the beginning of another. The superior person rests into this knowing that keeping still is but a moment of pause, observation, and preparation of what is yet to come.

A Practice Called Earth Reverence

Stepping out of the celebration of summer, the permitted passion of the Southern shield that comes with childhood, is not something many of us want to do. It requires a death, of sorts, or the release of the joy we know in the unselfconscious moments of our youth, and then the embrace of a more serious reality. Our unselfconsciousness is lost to the greater concern of needing to know who we are, how we serve, and if we might possibly hope for Love from another.

How do we begin?

After the grief that's required to truly let go, there is the possibility of an Earth Reverence practice. By this I mean communion with what is Holy in earth form, in your body, in the food you eat, and the ground you walk on.

So the first steps in a Reverence Practice begin in the body, and ask you to seek connection and intimacy with your own self. This is done with ancient tools for grounding and centering that are taught in Part II of this book. One begins by dropping in and orienting from a felt sense.

From here, we can reach into the imaginal realms and seek resolution of old memories held in the cells, both our own and those of our ancestors. The implications of such clearing are profound and leave one not only with a greater sense of presence and ease, but also clarity of purpose and sense of belonging.

Beyond that, those spiritual implications of feeling more present and connected, you find ease in your own body. It begins with the simple exercise of grounding and centering taught later in this book.

When Reverence for one's own body, one's own thoughts, and one's own reality is restored and respected, we begin to interact not only with ourselves differently—affording ourselves a sense of respect and attention that we deserve—but also to others and to the very ground we stand on.

Raspberry Leaf Tea – *as Anthony William, author of Life-Changing Foods says, raspberry leaf tea is "the ideal reproductive system re-organizer and protector, supports adrenal gland production of estrogen, progesterone, and testosterone, and it feeds the thyroid gland with critical nutrients for replenishment."*

2 tbsp dried raspberry leaf
2 cups water

Place leaves and water in small saucepan over stove. Bring to a boil. Reduce and simmer for some 3 minutes. Turn off flame and let sit for 20 to 40 minutes. Drink hot or cold. Add honey and or oat milk.

Sometimes, when life is hard, my world blossoms with the surprise of a visit from a student I once had the privilege of teaching. This is the true harvest. The return of a seed I once planted with a thought, a gesture, a conversation, or a lecture comes back in full fruit. This week Ruby, 22 years old already, wrote to tell me she had found her way farther north in Ireland and arrived in a monastery where they have allowed her to stay, exchanging room and board for her work in their gardens. The monks have even invited her to join them in their morning and evening prayers which, she writes, "is bringing into such clarity to the ways that I pray."

Now, this is a young woman whom I met when she was 15 years old. She fell like a star from the sky, in circular motion to the front of my moccasin stand at the San Rafael farmer's market.

"Oh Mother, please- please, may I have a pair of these for my birthday?!" she exclaimed. Two weeks later, on her fifteenth birthday, she arrived at my front door to collect her moccasin boots and begin what we came to call an apprenticeship.

Initially, we both thought she was there to learn leatherwork and to sew. But our Friday mornings in the studio were filled just as much with food and discourse. It started with the story of her family falling apart when she was 13. "Let's just be real," she says to me as her story falls out of her…the pieces that hurt, and how she came to live with it all. She told me about not eating and running for miles on end to try to make her way through it. She recalled with me the teachers who had "seen" her and reached out to bring her back to some form of balance, when there was none.

But now things at her mother's had stabilized. She had found her way into a high school program that was self-directed and gave her school credits for things like this, coming to spend Fridays with me doing leatherwork.

Her "realness" brought mine out, and all of our doubts, longings, and insecurities found ground there on the floor of the studio, between hides, patterns, and shoes. We traced, cut, stitched, laced, packaged, and shipped off shoes of all sizes. Baby shoes with feathers (ugghhhh, horrible idea. Of course the babies pulled the feathers off!). Women's shoes and boots with button shells. Men's moccasins, which were our favorite. The meditation of doing a larger man's shoe seemed to provide us both with just the right amount of space to breathe and really rest into the process of making a shoe.

Making shoes, we found, was not really just about making shoes. There's a meditation within it. From finding how to fit the shape of the shoe onto the deer hide in just the right way that remembers that this material is the back of an animal, to then cutting—precisely and directly—to then lining up the stitches to sew. There is no room for mistakes or mis-cuts. Every gesture you make is exposed. This requires the utmost focus and attention. One must be completely centered throughout the entire exercise. So, we called it a meditation. One's state of presence and ability to focus is instantly exposed. It was Ruby who showed me the poetry of it all. And the shoes that reminded me that the state of one's mind and one's heart shows clearly in the work that comes out of her hands.

I think I lured her back, week after week, with lunch. When I heard that her boyfriend had asked where she learned to cook, and she said, coyly with that sparkle in her eye, "Mer! I told him you taught me how to cook!"

"I taught you?" This was so astounding to me that I finally stopped.

I stopped my efforting to get it all done, the cooking, the cleaning, the mothering, and trying to be "connected" in a world designed to pull us all apart. I could finally let go of it all.

"But what did I even teach you?" I asked.

"You've taught me how to listen. How to pay attention."

"Yes?"

"To take the simple ingredients and put them together in these magical ways that brings it all to life. Like, who is it, Tita? in *Like Water for Chocolate*."

My world now has come to a halt. Everything I could hope to give has been given to this gem named Ruby. And so, she started to call me her godmother and leave me baskets of fresh vegetables on the porch.

Today, on my phone I have a picture of a fruit crumble she had prepared for the monks in Ireland.

"What a cook you are!!" they tell her. Where on earth did you learn?" they ask. "Mer," she writes, "I lit up telling them all about you."

What was in those bowls we ate for lunch here on Fridays anyway? How I ever achieved such an honor, I will not know.

Prepare Me Pickled Pink Onions - *these pungent, crunchy onions make an incredible addition to any salad dish. Onions themselves are cleansing, assisting in the removal of parasites and pathogens such as viruses and bacteria. They are an ideal food for the fall, as they cleanse and nourish the lungs and colon, thereby preparing you for winter and the health challenges that arise. I like to have a jar in the fridge for adorning lunches and dinners. Ruby loves them.*

One red onion, washed, peeled sliced thin
1/2 cup seasoned rice wine vinegar
1/2 cup water
A bay leaf

Some peppercorns if you have them
Delight
Empty jar to fit sliced onions

Bring a kettle of water to boil. Slice onion and place into a colander in sink. Pour boiling water over onions to tenderize. Place in jar, and cover with combination of water and vinegar. Cover with lid, and leave on counter for 2 days before refrigerating. Lasts about 2 to 3 weeks in fridge. Excellent in salads, on eggs, vegetable bowls, tacos…whatever you like.

DIGESTION: THE RELATIONSHIP BETWEEN FIRE AND EARTH

In Ayurveda, we say that good health and good digestion cannot be separated. How you receive and process food directly informs how well you are. This is true on a molecular level: how well your digestive systems can break down the nutrients in the food you eat and filter them on a cellular level into your blood, bones, organs, and other regulatory systems of your body. And on a spiritual level: how do you receive what you are given to feed from?

In Ayurveda we talk about Agni, the digestive fire. Strong digestive fire is considered an essential part of being well. It helps to digest and assimilate food into the body to build and maintain balance in and between the organ systems. Agni must be supported through food, herbs, and lifestyle.

Likewise, a healthy appetite and hunger, as we classify them in the West, are essential ingredients for staying well. Instead of suppressing our appetites and limiting food intake, as many of us are taught to do, we could be celebrating them. We could learn to recognize that a healthy appetite and ability to take in diverse foods supports our growth, our immunity, our endocrine system, and ultimately our relationship with the earth.

Without proper digestion and assimilation, we can't build the building blocks of the body and its diverse systems for maintaining health. This is understood across fields of medicine, from basic biology and Western Nutrition, to Ayurveda and Chinese Medicine.

Basic Quinoa - *quinoa was called the "Mother Grain" by the Inka and has a nutritional profile equivalent to milk in terms of protein. It can be a wonderful alternative to rice or even oatmeal as a breakfast dish. Like nuts and seeds, I find it hard to digest unless my Agni or "stomach fire" is fierce and turned on. Usually it's not. The requirement of a modern mother living in a single family home/social construct requires too* *much of me to have the inner resources to digest these things! My prayer is that you are not!! (otherwise, see digestive enzymes p 194)*

1 cup quinoa
1 1/2 cup water
Fire
Pinch of salt optional

Rinse quinoa in sieve. Place with water in a heavy saucepan over medium heat on stove. Once it boils, turn heat down to a simmer. Let cook 20 minutes. Stir and let cool. Optional: salt to flavor

I seem to be thinking too much.

The love I have lost.

The love I wish to have.

The conversation I had with a new "Love" last week.

My right eye starts to twitch and finally it's official: I am tired. Tired of thinking too much? Could be.

Then, there are the lists and lists of emails—so many. Every day. From everyone involved in the children's schools. Parents, teachers, businesspeople, and fundraisers. And the driving. Both to school AND to after-school activities, weekend games, and birthday parties. Rafa - soccer. Oliver - dance. Remi - Aikido. Alexei - seriously? I am supposed to sign up my three-year-old for after-school enrichment classes? And also know what is for dinner, lunch, and breakfast tomorrow? (We are not eating cereal, guys, sorry. Too hard on your digestion. I don't care if it says, "whole grains." They are not whole. They are processed. And I want you to have warm food to start the day. It is fall.)

"Mom!! We're out of toilet paper!" someone calls up to me. *And gas,* I think to myself. Yes. Thinking too much. Could be.

Ice cream: the go-to solution for overwhelm, confused hunger signals, and matters of the heart is no longer an option. The kids are watching and doing just as I am. So my overwhelm, longing, and need for comfort will have to find another way.

I open my computer instead. "Jonathon, Any chance we can set up an appointment for Cranial Work sometime soon? Right eye twitching. Need a tune-up."

"Yes. Tuesday. 2 pm? I can come there," he says. Phew.

Then I remember Chalita: affordable Acupuncture in a community/group setting just over the hill, only $40 away. Chalita has ushered me through numerous cases of poison oak, fatigue, colds, night sweats, menstrual irregularities, delayed births, and exhaustion. Acupuncture has seen me through 30 years of life, offering up treatment for riddles in my complete mind-body, when Western Medicine would have preferred clinical tests, long conversations, and a series of pills.

"Chalita! My right eye is twitching."

"Ahhh, the spleen," she says. "Overthinking, processing, analyzing. Yes, I see."

She already knows what to do. Within in moments, she knows the course of action and is carefully, yet swiftly, placing needles in select points on my body. There is a needle along my spleen channel, just inside my lower leg. It is a point I have been working with for 30 years now, ever since my period didn't come. It is called Spleen 6 and is a "meeting point of the three lower yin" channels. Like a confluence of rivers who meet in one point, it is the meeting place of the liver, kidney, and spleen meridians, the energetic power houses that command the deep internal feminine energy, the energy that holds the ground for action and activity. And there is a needle on a point at the top of my foot, just beneath my big and second toes. I know it to be a "Command Point" called "Supreme Rushing" that not only helps to release energy that is stuck along the liver meridian, but also helps to tonify the body at the end of summer. So, our timing is just right.

In Chinese Medicine, the organs are thought of not only as dense physical entities that fill the cavity beneath the ribs and have specific roles in moving blood, processing hormones, absorbing and sorting food and nutrients, and filtering and transporting blood, etc. They are also thought of as energetic entities that receive both thoughts and feelings and translate them into your physical space, your physical reality. So when a needle goes into a point on your body, it is with the intention of not just resolving a physical condition, but also treating into the antecedents of that condition, the things that came before, and those that will follow. Assume that you are a bodymind and that this mind exists up into the storehouse of your virtues, then steps down energetically into your feeling and their pathways down into your body. Make sense?

Meridians, which we name for the organ that they eventually step down into, are like rivers and creeks in our bodies. They carry currents of energy, like rivers carry water. Sometimes, they get dammed up. Initially, this impacts you on a thought/feeling level. Eventually, it will manifest on a physical level. Acupuncture needles help to release the dam and restore the flow of life force. It's simple and effective.

In 40 minutes I am up out of the chair and walking away. My eye is no longer twitching, and I rested into a sound sleep that night.

 **Get it Together Sesame Dressing** - *this rich and nourishing dressing offers amino acids, proteins, and good fats, while also giving weight to a salad and bringing it all together. The weight and creaminess of this dressing is even better when it's warm. I am convinced it ensures a good night's sleep. It may be the high magnesium and other mineral content that helps me sleep. Or, it may be that this dressing, though dairy-free and vegan, is almost like drinking mother's milk.*

1/2 cup sesame seeds, unhealed
1/2 cup olive oil (combine with sunflower oil for a lighter taste, if desired)
1/2 cup water
Depth
1/2 cup seasoned rice wine vinegar

Combine sesame seeds and oil in a blender and blend until smooth. Add water and vinegar, and blend until creamy and white. Pour over salads, rices, greens, cooked vegetables.

Love My Life Lunch Bowls - *eating at home is a privilege, and one I will work fiercely to not give up. It allows for deep connection, not only with place and my home, but also with myself, and what I bring into my home to feed my beloveds. Lunch is a memory. It brings together the pieces I have gathered over the week to play with as nourishment. Lunch bowls are an observation of this, the way observation is described in my I Ching - both an arrival point and a moment of pause, where one takes in the beauty of what has been achieved, just before it is manifested or shared.*

Cooked quinoa (or rice) from leftovers in fridge (quinoa recipe p 136), a carrot, pickled pink onions, mixed greens washed, walnuts (soaked overnight and slow roasted until dry all the way through soaked nut recipe, p 141), get it together sesame dressing (p 139), olive oil, lemon. Combine in a bowl, cover with sesame dressing, and flavor with salt and gratitude. Eat with a fork or your fingers. Maybe a tortilla or some other bread on the side.

Remi and Alexei, who were spending the night at their dad's, are home now and begging to take bikes over the grade to horse hill. A bike ride! That sounds heavenly enough for a Sunday morning. Alexei will sit on the back of my bike, and Remi can ride himself. Yes!! Let's go.

We set off with no snacks or water, just huge excitement to see if we'll find horses feeding on the other side. It's 9 am, breakfast time for the horses. There they are, in the paddock, feasting on hay.

There is an ease in each of us as individuals today and as a group. It's just the three of us. The horses feel it and let us approach, even as they eat. The speckled gray "young guy," Remi calls him, invites us over and entertains a rub, even as a younger dark brown mare rebuffs us and walks off.

"It's ok," I tell the boys. "If you don't want someone near you, that's what you do, walk away."

I remember a counselor in college needing to teach me that. If something makes you uncomfortable, you walk away. That's the healthy response! I don't think I learned that when I was younger. And often, when I was bold enough to state how I felt, I was told not to feel that way. "Don't be sad," "There's nothing to be afraid of," "No, no, no, that's not true. Everything is ok." Often, it wasn't. And eventually I learned to not trust what I was feeling.

Horses are therapy. They have a way of reflecting back exactly what they feel. The sheer power of their physique, and the mirror they offer with their body language, is enough to make us see what we are feeling. So, any connection we can establish and maintain with a horse can be healing. Of course, that's what I think about when I go to see horses!

Remi and Alexei just want to feed them. Touch them. Get up and ride them. Without a saddle, of course, the way I used to dream of riding a horse. The way I think any young person imagines riding a horse. Once it's saddled and restrained, the mystique and mystery fade. But we weren't allowed to get up on them, so we got on our bikes instead.

We biked down to the school playground. I taught the boys about "crashing parties" when we happened upon a children's biking birthday party with a tricks circuit course for little bikers. Remi jumped in, but I couldn't convince another little one to hand over his bike for Alexei to ride the circuit. And the boys couldn't convince me to go to the party table to "share in" the snacks. So, we kept going.

An apple tree on the way home, near horse hill, was just starting to drop its fruit. "Here guys!! How about some fresh apples?"

"Yes. Yes." They agreed, and we filled my sweater with apples for now and for later, and biked back up and over the hill home.

 Soaking and Slow Roasting Nuts - *nuts are a wonderful snack, sure to nourish and fill and not spike your blood with sugar. But nuts, and seeds, can be hard to digest. When things are hard to digest, they actually require more energy to process and may not move fully through the digestive system. This recipe helps ease digestion and release the nutritional benefits of any nut.*

1 1/2 cups almonds
or
1 1/2 cups walnuts
3 to 4 cups water
1 tsp fine sea salt
Patience

Place nuts in a large bowl and soak overnight. Drain. Rinse. Spread nuts on cooking sheet on top of wax paper and lightly salt if desired. Place into an oven set at lowest temperature possible. Toss on occasion for approximately 8 hours or until dry and crunchy.

THE MEDICINE OF PLACE

Somewhere along the way, in my studies abroad and global apprenticing, I noticed that what I really craved, as much as the learning about language, culture, and how medicine lived inside of it, was the feeling these people had of "home." When I say "these people" I refer to the people who lived, breathed, worked, played, laughed, danced, and exercised life inside of the container they called home. There was a surrender and a belongingness I didn't feel in my life. My life as a modern being who sought experiences, knowledge, growth, and work *beyond* the place I called home.

So I came to love my travels and the people I met inside of them—as much for the novelty and adventure as for the privilege of feeling what it was like to be rooted. To call a place home.

Finally, as an adult with children, I learned that my small, everyday practices, the ones where I connect completely with the Earth I stand on, are what it takes to root in place. To make a place home. The garden, the bike rides, the outing with the boys to see the horses over the hill, the interdependency with my neighbors and with the trees in the neighborhood—these are what offer the possibility of really feeling at home here. If I don't cultivate those relationships, the immediate ones, the ones that are simple and obvious, then I will never feel the roots I so envied in my travels abroad.

Medicine, then, in the words of a respected healer and medicine maker Darcey Blue:

"The awareness of medicine is as old as humans have been walking around on this great green earth. It comes to us through our senses, the scent of a blossom in the wind, the way certain items catch our vision in just the right light, the taste of bitterness, through song whispered in the wind, or a question in the heart, a suffering or pain that guides us to seek support. This awareness is not dependent on a book, or a scientific study, nor even a species name or facts passed on from teacher to student. It is with us always, we only have to make ourselves available to touch, taste, feel, wonder, connect, experiment. Trust that the wisdom and heart of our Earth Mother is reaching out to us through intuition. Nor does medicine have to be a bottle of tincture with specific doses and indication, but can be a connection that inspires, that strengthens and opens the heart of wonder within us. There really are no rules about how medicine comes to us, and how it works. It is guided by the healing impulse within the human heart and wise soul of nature." [1]

In the afternoon, we walked over to the garden at the Co-op to plant the sweet pea and nasturtium seeds we had been soaking overnight.

In the sweet silence of a home without children, I took the time yesterday to nick every seed with an exacto knife, as indicated on the pouch. It's careful work, where each hard and tiny seed has to be suspended between my thumb and forefinger and held tightly enough that when I poke it with the knife it won't slip. So each seed gets held in a firm, clear, personal way. This helps them to open and germinate with more success, so it says on the package. At Chispas farm in New Mexico, they will say that you could also lick them, "to give them a head start and establish a connection—to let them know who is going to care for them." (*The Magazine.* Southwest Contemporary, Aug. 2019) This kind of intimate contact excites them toward life. And the whisper, "safe journey," down the row where they have been planted offers a blessing for greater success, and perhaps, on our end, greater commitment to them.

So today, one by one, or three by three, I placed them into the small holes I had poked with my fingers into the fresh soil in the hanging pockets that cover a south-facing wall at the Co-op.

"Kurt!!! Please turn the irrigation on," I am still saying to him today, a few days later. "I have pricked, and licked, and poked, and prayed to these seeds," I said. "If the water doesn't start today, we may lose them." This is a heavy concept in a world of non-essential commitments.

The boys made mischief at the water table (Yes!! A table at arm's length for a three-year-old to splash in the water on hot days! It is flowing freely and abundantly next to my dry dirt pockets), while I planted the seeds. Some mint, too, that I had gathered from a community garden next to a soccer game Rafa played last week. (When it's in its pure form, it doesn't offend like a breath mint or gum and is a wonderful leafy surprise in a salad or a loose leaf tea.) Its tips have flowered purple, and it is seeding. So I collected last spring's "waste" and planted it before we rushed off to another soccer game.

"The body of a garden is not so different from that of a human. We are both ecosystems, both in a delicate balance, both averse to toxic chemicals, unsympathetic knives, incorrect doses of nutrition and food. Yes, we can adapt. Yes, there are times when disease can be cut out and removed, and this saves a life. Yes, we are able to assimilate and digest medicine that is not just right and even thrive after that. But what if the garden has a gardener that is sensitive to the needs of each plant and responds with deep listening and precision to those needs? How then would the garden grow?" —Merrill Page

---

After Chalita's Acupuncture treatment, I later received a Craniosacral treatment. With it, all of my longing went away. That was what I noticed most when I got up off of the table. That feeling that haunts me of wanting something more than what is. When it lets go, I feel ease and fullness. As if everything that was holding in my body or clenched in my jaw has let go. I don't even notice the holding or clenching until it has been removed. But once it's gone, my feet feel different on the floor. My face feels softer and my skin more supple. My ability to be complete where I am is easy. I'm reminded of a world I learned in the years I danced tango: surrender.

The session started with a simple question, "What are you needing?"

"Well, I reached out because my right eye was twitching. It's better now, after an Acupuncture treatment. Chalita treated my spleen and did some liver points," I told him.

"Mmm," Jonathon nods. He is no stranger to this language, having just completed a full degree at the College of Acupuncture in Oakland. "I am noticing perhaps a twist in your sphenoid," he adds. He's looking at my forehead and the bone behind my eyes. With his eyes, sensitivity, and years of cranial study and practice, he can assess my body physiology for balance and energetic tone.

"Ok. Could be. I've been well, but tired. And we are going through so many transitions here at home," I said.

We talk another minute before I climb onto the table, fully clothed, as is done in Craniosacral work, and lie down, face up, on top of the sheets of a massage table.

He starts with a gentle touch at my shoulders, then moves down to my feet and ankles to see if they are even and to assess for tension and fluidity. The touch is gentle and, like Acupuncture, assessment is part of the treatment. It's his ability to see inside of me, my energetic field and my body physiology, that begins to effect change. It's quantum physics. Matter changes when it's observed.

Now Jonathon, he has a magic way where he offers up what he sees/or feels/or hears. It's what we are taught in our Milne Training for Visionary Craniosacral Work®. "Don't miss the chance to tell your client/patient what you see," Hugh tells us. Your observation and insight may change his/her life. So today, Jonathon, in a language he knows that I speak, says to me, "It feels like maybe the left temporal bone is stuck or blocked. As if there is something you don't want to hear." Or the last time he worked on me, "I get the feeling you are a castle filled with treasures and not yet convinced the world is worth sharing them with."

These are the kind of morsels that torture and delight a patient like me, leading my vision inward, to inquiry, where it belongs. This is part of finding peace.

Like that time when Hugh Milne was teaching us to work with mandibles and teeth trauma through contacts inside of the mouth. He had his gloved hands, or fingers to be precise, resting on the tops of the teeth in my lower jaw.

"I get the sense you love to be kissed," he offers up.

These sorts of insights are, after all, the key to the magic.

"Ha," I express, as well as one can lying supine with gloved hands in their mouth. But then I can't stop. I am giggling and giggling, as quietly as possible because of the other 50 students and teacher/practitioners also working in the room. The more I realize what he just said, and that it is true, the more I laugh. I love to be kissed. I guess I hadn't realized that about myself. Until Now. Yes. It is true! I do love to be kissed, I think to myself, then struggle to direct my mind to another thought that will release me from the delight of hearing, and now knowing, this.

"Cranio-sacral Integration engages with the deepest healing forces, both within the body and in the surrounding matrix, in order to enable re-organization and re-integration of mind, body, and spirit, overcoming the depleting effects of trauma, injury, disease and stress and enabling profound transformation in health and wellbeing." —**Thomas Attlee, teacher and practitioner.**

So there are many layers and many possibilities within this discipline called Cranial Work. Its efficacy depends on one's willingness. Willingness to be seen. Willingness to surrender. Capacity to trust that they are safe, in present time, to feel whatever it is that is offering itself up to be felt.

"You can pay now. Or you can pay later," Sofia Diaz, my beloved Yoga teacher used to tell us. "But either way, you have to pay. You have to feel the pain for it to leave your body. There is no other way."

This is what I mean by willingness to feel. It's like our willingness to be held. And loved. If we can't let ourselves be held and loved, we are not able to be nourished the way a full-fledged human needs to be nourished. That's just how it is.

Lying on the table with Jonathon saying nothing now, my body reorganizes itself around the mid-line. This is what we call it in cranial work. It is the center place occupied by the spinal column. A practitioner's touch is supposed to help regulate the fluid bathing the spinal column, the craniosacral fluid. It flows at a slow and rhythmic pace that nourishes the nerves and helps regulate the nervous system. It is also called the breath of life.

Craniosacral therapy can be described in so many ways, from esoteric and metaphysical terms, like "breath of life," to osteopathic or scientific terms, like "torsion in the spheno-basalar joint." And the shape and condition of the bones within themselves and in relationships to each other impact us on both a physical and a metaphysical level. So, when we touch or receive touch with this level of awareness, we have the ability to alter reality within the physiology and beyond. That's just how it is. Then it's up to the patient to perceive and choose to embody the changes in his/her life.

Jonathon continued the treatment with a contact at my sacrum, or tailbone. Here, with his hand, he can unwind any tension or compression along my spinal column, alleviating pain or discomfort along a vertical axis up into my occiput, which is the bone at the back of my head said to be a mirror to the sacrum. His contact feels gentle and kind, but also clear and safe. There is "a listening" to it. We are taught to listen to the bone and how it is in relationship to the other bones it is touching. To listen to the fluid and how the cranial tide moves or doesn't move along the spinal column. To the energy and how it expands or contracts, expresses or doesn't express, through the immediate bodily systems and beyond. It is slow work. It takes time.

Listening takes time. But it's just like talk therapy or counseling where once somebody has expressed themselves and feels heard, they can let go. They can move out of the narrative that has them trapped in repetition or some contracted state and expand into present time. The body is like this: it wants to be heard. Seen. Received. Understood. Nudged in just the right way where it can release what it is holding and move on. A good practitioner does this.

We finish with a contact at my head. His hands are over my ears listening into the many expressions there, from the state of the temporal bones to the health and plasticity of the cranial nerves that have pathways into the ears. Entire treatments can be done simply with a contact at the ears, listening and directing intention to clear blocks and resolve issues from tinnitus to headaches, a twitching face, to grinding teeth. The implications are infinite, and the treatment so subtle.

I have to get right up off the table when we are done and dart off to school to pick up boys. But I don't forget to notice the contact my feet make with the ground when I get up off the table, so solid and clear. Or the feeling in my face, that is let down and tired, like after a good night's sleep. The heaviness in my body is indisputable and delicious. The fatigue I can actually feel now is rich and re-centering. I couldn't feel it before.

It's easier to sit that evening outside and watch the boys hit baseballs in the backyard and jump on the trampoline. I sit easily there and feel a togetherness with them that I do not have when I am not cared for in these intimate and gentle ways.

HARVESTING TREASURES FROM WITHIN

"These are the kind of morsels that torture and delight a patient like me, leading my vision inward, to inquiry, where it belongs."

As an adult, I have come to truly savor the moments of surrender, when I can let go of how I think things need to be and simply feel what is. There, when my body is at ease, and my mind lets go, is the moment of grace. It's where our vision can turn inward, to inquiry and observation. Such is the lesson of the Western shield, and the requirement of an adolescent.

At first though, it's torture. Who really wants to let go of that ecstatic moment of movement, engagement, and sensual fulfillment to pause and look inside? Unless we are guided and taught to notice the treasures of an internal, self-reflective practice, the idea is anathema, and the exercise is impossible. It is the job of a culture, and the adults who inhabit it, to teach their young to do this. When we do not, they cannot harvest the gifts that they bring to us.

It's that simple, but the ritual practices required to really teach our adolescents how to look in, to feel, to notice, and to bring out the gifts hiding there inside of them are not laced into our cultures the way they were in older, earth-based cultures. Luckily, new forms of earth-centered therapies are reclaiming them and offering outdoor programs with supervised camping solos where our youth can discover, in an embodied way, what "old" cultures used to know.

 All of My Longings Went Away Dates and Rice/Flax milk - *in the afternoon, when I think I need to eat something, even when I am not hungry, this always fits the bill. Dates, as you know from chapter 2, are 'the way' to a healthy gastrointestinal tract, balanced blood sugar, and a clear, incisive mind. You don't even need to put it in a blender, add frozen banana, or cocoa, or vanilla as other recipes suggest. But you can if you want to!*

2 dates
1 glass milk (1/2 rice + 1/2 flax)
Serve and delight

And then, there is Shamanic healing. These come with outbursts of giggles. Not mine, but Remi's. They're fresh and new and light the air like chimes in the winter.

This time, it was my mother who brought the Shaman to us.

"Fernanda, who you remember lost her son in the drowning accident some years ago, she swears by this lady. Fernanda was at a point where really nothing was helping her, and she did not want to go on living. Well, she went to see this Shaman, and it changed her entire life around," my mother said.

Elizabeth, the Shaman, writes on her website: one session can do what 10 years of therapy aspire to. I have found these sorts of statements to be true.

"Can we send Remi?" I ask my mom.

"Sure, what for?"

"Oh, I guess to help him recover from some of the trauma we all lived when our family came apart," I said. "He's clingy and fearful still. And he is always talking so loudly. He can't seem to moderate his voice."

I took him to see a Craniosacral therapist a couple of years ago (he was four), and I couldn't believe what he said when he got off of the table.

"What was it like?" I asked him.

"It was like she was untying my head," he replied.

My jaw dropped. I can imagine his head got all tied up, with the way his parents used to yell at each other. He was better then, for a while.

And he trips over his own feet too much. I wonder if she can help that?

A Shaman's work is soul work. Shamans, doctors in their own right, understand where metaphor and medicine meet. They know that something that is out-picturing into the world has its origin in something invisible, dark, deep. Perhaps of this lifetime. Perhaps before. So, physical dis-ease and discomfort is met with the mind and cured with energy. It takes sensitivity, *extreme* sensitivity, and perception to be able to identify just what the "right" medicine is for the person who is ill. It may be as simple and straightforward as a healing tea or plant. Either its "pharmaceutical" constituents or its vibrational profile could be the key to healing the person. Or it may be as intangible and far-off as a distortion in their energetic field. A fold, a crimp, a twist, a dart. It must be removed, and the field smoothed out and "re-lit" again.

This is the work of a Shaman. To see. And to be able, through this perception, to heal. So Shamans, though traditionally found in original or Indigenous cultures, are appearing in new places and forms. They are here in our cities now. These people who can "see" and, in this seeing and with their command of power and energy, can also heal.

When a soul is harmed it retreats. Energy folds in on itself, and one's true expression of health and vibrancy can't come through. In time, if the energy stays blocked, the darkness obscures our path. Our purpose. A Shamanic treatment on the layers of the energetic body can help open the blocks and restore the person to their own body space. What results is a new sense of self. Even joy. Delight. And once that returns, one can begin to find his/her way again. In this walk, health begins to return.

For Remi, his recovery after the treatment came as giggles. And the sudden ability to whisper, which he didn't have before. And a new capacity to push back, at all of us, when we encroach upon "his space." This will take some getting used to!

How Energy Medicine Works

In addition to my own observations, and those of us in the field of Complementary and Alternative Medicine, the scientific research on the subtle energy field's response to human intention is mounting and has been for 50 years. James Oschman, a respected biophysicist, biologist, and author, provides both scientific and clinical insights on the scientific basis of Mindbody Medicine in his wonderful book, *Energy Medicine, The Scientific Basis.* Donna Eden, a respected practitioner and author in the field of Energy Medicine states, "While the subtle energies cannot move a needle on a gauge, many healers know how to engage them to restore health and vitality." She cites Tiller's work at Stanford University that has developed the technology to measure an energy field beyond the electromagnetic spectrum and show how this field responds to human intention.[2]

"Bio-electricity" is another word that cutting edge osteopaths who are working to bridge medical practices with physics and energetics, such as Dr. Michelle Veneziano, are using to refer to the energetic pulses that translate consciousness and energy to health and healing. Michelle Veneziano, like Larry Dossey, Dean Radin, and Russel Targ, further applies concepts of Quantum Physics, wave vs. particle, to help us understand how energy can so profoundly affect matter. Their work provides resources for those wishing to satiate the mind's desires to understand the mechanics of how Energy Medicine "works" and can be translated into modern medicine. These doctors/practitioners offer us clinical research and language to describe phenomena that are new to our ways of thinking.

While researchers practiced in the protocols of controlled scientific studies map out and perform the rigors required of Western Science and Modern Minds, I will dance with the unseen surprises of long distance healings from a respected Shaman on the 8th floor of a sky rise in New York City.

"Alice! We are out of town next week. Do you think you could keep an extra eye on the garden?" I asked my favorite new mom at the Co-op.

"Sure," she said, in her solid and glowing way. It's an enthusiastic response. But grounded and clear. Like she knows she's committing to something more than her already massive commitment of two children, ages one and a half and four, her Co-op jobs, her work outside her home, her home, and her husband. I like this about her.

"What do you need?" she asks.

"I have just planted new seeds in the pockets in the back. Will you make sure they stay damp?" I said.

"Yes, ok."

"The garden in the front, there are a few new pots with seeds, in the front at the entrance where the trees are."

"Ok," she nods.

"When you can," I add. "I know it's a lot."

I spot Laurie on the way out and ask her, too, not so concerned now with loyalties as I am with keeping my seeds alive and sprouting. Alice walks out as Laurie walks in. They connect and coordinate.

Gardens do not combine easily with modern life. Seedlings are like babies. Once you give birth to them, you must care for them, 24 hours a day, 7 days a week. I remember my brother saying so many years ago, when my mom was making an excuse for eating a dessert, saying she was on vacation, "Britty," he said to his step-mother, "You are never on vacation from yourself."

It's like this with our children and our gardens. Once they are living, they need our continuous care.

There is something happening inside of the word "organic." It is called 'TRUST.' It is an idea that is echoing through a 52.5 billion dollar industry, engaging the imagination and hope of young people throughout the world, and uniting them in their quest to "save the planet."

Here in Mexico, we come to stay in the "Organic Dome" five kilometers down a treacherous dirt road inside of the jungle. It's an architect's expression of his dream for a sustainable building model right outside of its opposite - Cancun.

All they promised us was "organic," but inside of that, the idea: we are safe here. Safe from toxic chemicals, safe from building materials that are unsustainably sourced and will be harmful when their short lives are over, and they start to disintegrate. Safe from air conditioning and the toll it takes on the local ecosystem, the individual, and the planet. Safe from people who, when they travel, seek to carry with them their ways instead of exploring and embracing local ways.

We are not safe from the mosquitoes which were so thick and hungry last night at dinner that we had to take our food inside. Neither the natural nor the toxic heavy-duty mosquito repellent stood a chance next to the old local way: SMOKE. The man in the kitchen making our dinner finally set a piece of cardboard on fire to smoke them out. But it was too late, we were already on our way to our room.

We are also not safe from the tarantulas, two of which we sighted. We had just parked our car and stepped out to see the monkeys when I noticed one crossing my path. The boys hurried to see, an excitement which stopped the next car driving by. The man who stepped out of the car came over and picked it up.

"No son venenosas?" "Aren't they poisonous?!" I said to him in Spanish.

"Yes, but I know how to handle them," he replied as he turned the spider over and pressed a bottle cap against its fangs to release the venom there. Then, he put the spider back down, this time at the edge of the forest where it would be safe from cars.

Nor are we safe from our own ideas, that the ice here could make us sick, or to avoid fresh foods like salads and raw vegetables that could be contaminated by "bad" water and make us sick. Twenty years ago, when I lived in Latin America, this was more true. Today, we ate tacos from a street stand and drank their iced watermelon and lemon aqua frescas. I have my grapefruit seed extract with me, in case our tummies start to gurgle.

The fear of local food that I once carried in me when I traveled seems to have done me more harm than good. Not only did it keep me away from the organic (meaning here: unfolding naturally) offerings of someone who called this place "home" and knew the alchemy of making food from its fruited seeds, but it also had me taking apart the music and balance of a meal. I would eat just a tortilla with rice or avocado, but miss the fresh greens, tomatoes, or cilantro that are meant to be with it. Or worse, I would eat crackers, instead of fresh fruit. Packaged food instead of food offered right up out of the ground I was walking on. This never ends in a happy story. In Spain, when I was 13, it ended in depression and Anorexia.

But we are here now, and these sorts of fears and illusions have been released.

Our dinner tonight came together a bit like our day, in broad strokes and gestures. It started like this:

"Mom, can we please go out on the bikes?" Rafa asked.

After the long flight and car rides yesterday, all of us were eager to be out and moving down that dirt road just outside our door and bordered by solid, pulsating jungle.

"Okay, yes. I'm not sure if we can get to the beach, through all of the walled complexes and barricades along the highway, but let's try," I said to them.

Each of us had a bike. Alexei rode on the back of mine, through riddled roads of potholes, butterflies, an occasional agave plant, and touçan. Our joy was as thick as the mosquitoes. But on the other side of the highway, we were turned away. The barricade had a sign on it: Only Suppliers and Collaborators. Meaning servant/service entry only.

So we had to come back for the car. The car afforded us respect. At the barricade this time, five km farther down the road, they lifted the gate without even asking who we were. Now we could make our way into a place we might call beach. It was rocky coastline after all, covered in brain coral and fossilized stone. Succulents and flowers grew out of the rocks. The ocean felt fierce and the rocks sharp, but just beyond there was a coral beach and a tide pool where we could rest. And are those trilobites!?

I swam out into a reef where the sea fans and coral reached up, almost to scratch me, as extensive and shallow as it was. But the water was warm, receptive, and just deep enough. I let it hold me. "I am safe," I said to myself and tried to imagine it was true, there in the open water!

The boys begged for snorkels and masks, so we wandered farther down the road to the restaurant with a beach. DIVE SHOP: CLOSED. At least for today. It turns out, our goggles worked perfectly in the end. We had everything we needed.

Simultaneously, we gathered juice and bananas from the corner market. Limes and tomatoes. An avocado from the fruit stand. Two dozen warm tortillas wrapped in paper from the car selling lunch out of its trunk to the workers at the hotel next door. They are made by soaking dried kernels of corn in a large pail with a piece of lime (limestone), the stone beneath the surface of earth we are walking on, here in the Yucatan. It softens the corn for grinding, but it also provides the calcium we all need in our bodies to regulate our nervous systems and build our bones. They are a cornerstone of the Indigenous diet, the stones from which they feed.

On our way home, we stopped for a roasted chicken at a kitchen on the corner of the main drag in town where a young woman served meals for men coming home from construction sites at dusk. POLLO ASADO $150 pesos, whole. It had been roasting all day inside of her wood burning grill, cooked through so well that I found myself chewing on the bones and marveling at the taste of the land echoing through them.

It comes together just this way, when I am willing. All of the pieces that call to me, whispering like a warm breeze against my hard and protective adult skin, have a place. And when I receive them and allow them to come together on their own, they do, in just the right way. They themselves find a balance, and it's in this relational and easeful balance that I am well. Of course this requires trust, and food that is given and taken directly from the earth, without trucks and air conditioning in between.

I put the ensalada together with the tomato and picante onto my tortilla. Then some chicken and lime. The heat and acid of the salsa balance the richness of the roasted meat and leaves me only wanting for some fresh cilantro. And a tequila, or mezcal perhaps.

 Soften My Vision Mezcal - *because when you play with all of the elements, you temper your fear for the unknown. With permission, the grips of resistance fall away, and you stand more fully in your own power.*

4 oz mezcal
2 cubes of ice
A beautiful glass and a beach
Combine and sip, as quickly or as slowly as you wish

LEARNING TO FEEL SAFE

I am Safe.

I am Safe.

I am Safe.

"Repeat it to yourself over and over and over. At least three times a day. For at least eight weeks. It will transform your life," said the man who called in the angels to help hold space while he cleared my field. Say these words, not just because of what "you" have lived, but because of what we are all carrying in our cells. There's a fear and a rage from generations of abuse, amnesia, trauma—both collective and personal—that is ready to be washed away. If we can name it and see it, then we can let it go. And only when we let it go, will we be able to be fully here and capable of what we are here to do.

I did say those words to myself, some days. Many times. Other days not at all. Now, 10 or 12 weeks later, I am still doing it. And watching to see if my life feels different.

"Eco" is the word they use here, for educated travelers like us. They could call us hippies. Some would just say "we care."

Others, who know me better, might credit a love for elegance, quality, good design, and natural elements. Words like:

"Hippie Dome, Hipster Dome, and Organic Dome" do not do these rooms justice. They do not begin to capture the style and luxury of these buildings. The natural hand-harvested stone in the showers and in the sink, the smooth, sanded branches hanging on the adobe walls as hooks, the rounded plaster ceilings and woven-branch light fixtures. They celebrate the natural resources that abound here, making it not just a place to stay, but an art form and announcement for how to see and how to live.

Built in a "millinery" style to protect against bombs, earthquakes, storms, and decay, it offers an added sense of safety and protection. The builders packed cloth rolls with natural mud, like sausages, and wound them like snakes into the domes. It is truly a vision for sustainable building and a healthy life.

"Mom, can we go home?" Rafa said to me this morning. Twice.

We are sunburned. We are covered in mosquito bites from head to toe. And yesterday, in the lull of the afternoon, he was bored.

What are we doing here anyway? This is not home, or our homeland, and when we come, we eat, make waste, and, from an environmental viewpoint, we upset the balance of the ecosystem. Even as conscientious and conscious travelers, much of our food is wrapped in plastic, and we add one more car to the road. My boys sleep with air conditioning, and we go through multiple towels, clothes, and bed sheets that require washing daily. With all of the bodily discomfort and costs, to us and to the local environment, even I start to wonder, what are we doing here?

Then I arrive at the fruit stand in the median garden of the main road in town. "I'll just get some honey and fruit for later," I tell the boys. There are two small stands there, just across the street from the tortillera and supermarket where they sell soap, aspirin, brooms, bimbo bread, cookies, chips. The tables there are small, modest in size, compared to the farmers markets in California. But the offerings are so abundant, colorful, and diverse, that my jaw drops. Awe.

There are five types of local squash, plump, fleshy, and dark on the outside, like our winter squashes, but with a thinner skin. Bananas and avocados, large and small, beets that look like they come from soil spiked with vitamins and minerals, carrots, onions, tomatoes, all generously proportioned and perfectly shaped. Round. Plump. This table would make any "mama" want for a kitchen. The honey is on a platform of its own, clearly "homemade" and offered in recycled water bottles with no labels. Then, the bunches of green at the end of the table, the herbs catch my eye. Cilantro! I wish we had had some yesterday to balance the richness of the chicken. And, "What's this!?"

"Que es eso?" I ask the man behind the table with the dark honey-colored, open, wide face. I snap a piece from the top of the green bundle to smell it while waiting for his answer. "Ruda" we say at the same time. Yes, I know this smell. So well. From my days in Guatemala. "What do you all use it for?" I ask him in Spanish.

"Oh, any quantity of ailments," he replies. "Digestion, colds, fevers."

"How do you take it?"

"As a tea."

"So you have it here just for medicine?"

"Yes."

"Not for food recipes?" It's so strong, I can't imagine or remember ever tasting it in food, but I am intrigued by the fruit and vegetable man offering medicine at his table.

"No," he confirms. "Not in food."

The man at the table next to this comes over to explain. He takes a bundle and shakes it, as if shaking it over me. "This is how we use it. To ward off the spirits that are bad and make you sick." I nod, having been cleansed myself this way various times by Latin American healers/Shamans.

Ruda: Rue. I used to drink it daily as a tea when I lived in Guatemala with the Cachiquel Mayans, preventatively, for parasites. As well as to bring on my period, which, at age 22, still did not come on its own (without the help of birth control pills). "It's from the sage/salvia family, if I remember correctly," I said to him. He didn't know. Sages work magic on the female reproductive system.

Still, even when I was taking it daily at age 22 in Guatemala, my period never came. I stepped up my gynecological treatments with the Mayan midwife who massaged my uterus, or more accurately dug her hands into my lower abdomen with such force that I almost jumped of the table. Then she had me wrap myself in a rebozo, a kind of "girdle" made simply by tying a supple piece of cotton tightly around my hips to support my lower back and "keep my uterus up, in place." In three visits she claimed to have relocated my uterus and then accepted me as an apprentice.

She was responsible for tending to the women before, during, and after their home-births in the Western Highland region of Poaquil in 1997, when I was there. After our treatments, she let me travel on foot with her, up to one to two hours to visit mamas in their pre-natal months. Often, we arrived early with the sunrise in time for breakfast, homemade tortillas and steamed mountain greens, which we ate with the family on the mud floor of the kitchen where the baby would be born. Meanwhile, the tuj (mud hut) would be heating in the back, and once the water and the dome were warm enough, the midwife would bathe and massage the expecting mother. She even sang up into the expecting mama when she was kneeling over. Songs, and prayers, and warm breaths to soften the baby's pathway out into our earth world. This is how the Mayan midwife practiced "medicine" aiming to soothe both the mother and child, and prepare a clear path for the baby's arduous journey out.

All off this is what I find inside the scent of that Rue plant.

Then I spotted the fruit at the end of the table, jocotes!? "Are those jocotes!?!" I exclaimed.

"Yes," he nods. There is no translation for this fruit: jocote. I don't even have the words to describe it, but Oliver does. "Is this the one that's like the cross between an orange and a mango?" he asks. "Yes, I know it."

"That's it, exactly!" I say to him. "Only it's a little tart, and chalky I think. To me it tastes like fleshy vitamin C." It comes in the shape of an olive, about the size of a small plum, and has a flushed orange red skin that peels off like an avocado. You eat the flesh inside. The skin is thicker than a grape, but not as thick as the skin of an apple.

Oliver remembered the taste, but he still needed me to show him how to eat it. Just bite into the skin and rip it off with your teeth. The pit is so big and the meat of the fruit is so scarce that there's really no other way. And of course, it tastes better this way, without utensils or the formality of peeling.

Last night at dinner, Oliver had almost ended up in tears looking down at his plate of food. It turns out he wasn't quite sure how to eat it either. "You break up the pieces of chicken and use the tortilla like Tef in an Ethiopian restaurant," I told him, my frustration shifting to compassion realizing how foreign this was to him. It hadn't crossed my mind that eating this food would require instruction. A bowl of food with a base of rice, meat, and vegetables, then tortillas on the side. I have come up short here, many times, in teaching my children how to eat, not realizing that all of it requires instruction.

Smelling the rue and tasting the jocotes, then sharing them with my children, illuminated for me why we are here. We are here to remember these old ways of doing things. The medicines I have been studying now for so many years are alive here. They are still part of the living systems and people that birthed the recipes and hold the secrets of how and where we harvest, prepare, and take them. *We are here to remember.*

This place is fertile and absorbs all of us visitors because the Mayans have lived the way they have for so many years, in harmony with the place they call home.

 Pepita Salsa - *the oils of the pumpkin seeds are rich in good Alpha-linolenic fatty acids (omega 3s) and fats and will feed your cells, hair, and skin while centering your nervous system and helping to balance your hormones. The unique flavor of this salsa transports me directly to my days in the Western Highlands of Guatemala with the Cachiquel.*

1 cup of pumpkin seeds (roasted over medium heat on stove in large skillet until brown and popping)

2 plum tomatoes
1 pinch cayenne pepper
1 pinch salt
1 lime

Crush seeds in a mortar and pestle or in a blender until blended. Also, the tomatoes. Add seeds to tomatoes and rest of ingredients. Add enough wet ingredients to make into a wet paste. Salt to taste and serve with tortillas, eggs, chips, beans…whatever delights you.

THE MEDICINE AT YOUR FEET

Wormwood, Black Walnut, and Cloves

One of the most overlooked, mis-diagnosed, and emotionally charged digestive challenges, I think, are parasites and worms. Just the possibility of having a parasite or worms is embarrassing to most of us in the modern world. So there is shame attached to it. Then, our doctors and medical systems aren't often familiar, well-equipped, or even thinking about them as a cause of digestive distress, constipation, teeth grinding, anxiety, headaches, or skin rashes. But many of us, especially on our travels, are vulnerable to picking up something that sets off the balance of our digestive tract. A simple drug to expel parasites or worms (of which there are many, and each specific, so a diagnosis is required/recommended) or a longer commitment to a cleanse, can help correct a diverse set of symptoms, even when our stools haven't shown worms or parasites.

The herbs that cleanse parasites are the same as the ones that help bring on your period or stimulate birth!! I have always been intrigued by that. To prepare them, you make a decoction. (Recipe p 99)

Alternating diarrhea and constipation, teeth grinding, anxiety, hypersensitivity to sugar, caffeine, artificial light, noise, headaches, rashes, stomach aches, rings around the eyes, and recent travels out of the country would encourage me to inquire with my doctor about parasites and worms and explore herbs like wormwood, black walnut, and cloves.

It's comforting to have these sorts of tips, when you are drinking cold agua frescas from the corner vendors at the four-way lights on the highway, or getting dinner from the kitchen of the beautiful young woman with the metal roof and bamboo curtain walls, gas camping stove, and makeshift sink who cooks meals for the locals as chickens run through her legs.

The boys found their own bliss with masks and snorkels out on the coral reef after our visit to the fruit stand. Even the other tourists in life jackets with masks, and roped lines showing them when and how to float toward the promise of an underwater paradise, couldn't spoil the journey for them. Paradise it was. Just 30 feet out from the pure white sandy beaches, schools of fish, a barracuda, a star octopus, sting rays, giant greenback and logger head turtles, puffer fish, coral fans, and brain coral seem be thriving. With just a mask and a snorkel they entered a world as diverse and colorful as the one here on the land. Having them see this, even in the current state of imbalance in human:wildlife ratio, is why we are here.

We stopped again in town on our way home. School was just getting out and the uniformed children were walking home. One girl about Remi's age stepped to the side on the sidewalk to let us pass. She watched our every step and smiled at Alexei, who was walking barefoot. Her smile—big, broad, and bright—reminded me of the man who took the boys snorkeling and the other man who cooked us dinner last night. These people, who so much of the modern world think "have nothing," are the happiest, healthiest people in the world. They seem to know better than any of us that everything they really need is here within reach.

The clean salt water in the reef soothed our mosquito bites tonight. And the aloe, which is growing outside the door of our dome villa, is helping with the sunburns. So we all slept deeply into the idea that there is nowhere else we need to be just now.

"Mom!! They came, the baby turtles came! We got to help them into the water!" Rafa exclaims, now as open and bright as the people who have lighted our way these past few days. He is glowing with the excitement of his news.

"The turtles were born already!?" I asked, amazed that they were back from their beach excursion at this tender hour of 10 pm.

"Yes! A nest of 113. We even get to pick up the ones going the wrong way and help them into the water." They showed me a video of the turtles bubbling up out of the nest, 60 cm down inside of the sand. There are nests every few feet on the beach just in front of where we are staying. And it's birthing season.

Every night there are volunteers out on the beach to aid the turtles, greenback and logger heads, legendary animals that will one day weigh more than I do and potentially live twice as long, in getting to the sea. It used to be that they found their way by instinct and starlight down to the water. Now, with the multiple light shows projecting beams into the sky from behind, plus the electricity and various forms of cell towers and communications, the turtles inner GPSes are damaged, and they are running the wrong way. It's even more heartbreaking to witness in person than to hear and imagine. The local "raccoons" are perched in the woods, waiting to eat them. Yes, there are also predators in the sea. Only one in one thousand turtles will live to adult hood. It used to be one in one hundred.

This is truly a grand finale of our trip, without a light show, or a circus, or a restaurant. It's just a simple night on the beach watching these mythic creatures begin their journeys. Turtle medicine, they say in schools of Native American teachings, is the oldest symbol for Mother Earth. It embodies the medicine of Earth Mother and offers the possibility of deep healing and recuperation through connection to the earth itself. By grounding down and opening to receive the medicine of place and all it has to offer, one finds abundance and wellbeing again.

Awe-Inspiring Arugula - *I often begin my day with my favorite flavors of fall. The nutrients of homegrown greens and the mystique of a sacred apple create an aliveness that leaves me in awe of beauty and simplicity. And arugula grows as vigorously as weed, through all kinds of weather and climates, so it is true to a name like The Medicine at Your Feet. It's also delicious with papaya, instead of apple.*

1 to 2 cups washed arugula
1 fuji apple
1/4 cup raisins
(walnuts optional)
Beauty
Olive oil and lime

Combine ingredients and dress with olive oil and lime, or rice wine vinegar. Eat with your fingers, or a fork if you must.

The seeds that I soaked, pricked, licked, kissed, and prayed to did not sprout. The hanging pockets are not green, but brown and bare. Yes, it may be the oils in the pine needles that have fallen into them. Maureen says they make everything hard to grow back here. Or it may be that the water didn't come soon enough, or simply wasn't enough. But I left them after I planted them, so I wasn't watching, and I cannot say.

I take my heavy heart to the front garden. The beans are still abundant, and tomato plants are volunteering fiercely amongst the arugula, which is tall and my favorite shade of dark green. Then I smell the dill, which is mostly dead, but seeding. These are the seeds I can collect to plant again in the spring, with the squash seeds I have now from Mexico. Here in the garden, I get to live over and over the privilege of ushering in new life and helping that which dies fold back into itself. This is the privilege of a mother who, as my friend Cissi said to me once, "Must be prepared to have her heart broken every day." Such is the joy and grief of watching our children be born and grow, then swim off into the uncertain ocean of life.

The Indigenous people know this, Martin Prechtel will say. "The flute song in ceremonies is the voice of Nature in tears. It was the weeping of every female life form, animal and plant, who wept as her children grew and were harvested by life, eaten or replanted."[3] Which is why the sound of the flute belongs to the woman. The article itself, a long stick carved and molded to sing, this belongs to the man. But the weeping sound that his breath ushers forth when he plays it, that is the woman's. For it is she that knows that the child she conceives, grows, births, loves, and feeds into life will then step out to be eaten by the world. The flute helps her sing her grief.

What happens when the thing you love is lost? That which you have breathed your life into folds into its inevitable end. Something hungry and fierce comes to claim your illusion of balance and permanence. I hope you will cry the tears necessary to soften the ground beneath you, and release a fragrance that awakens the memory of yourself. And in this new air, you sense a hint of music, something that helps you remember what it feels like to dance. And, in that spark of memory, you feel, even if just a little, the sensation of your own heart. A whisper that inspires a smile, if only in your eyes. From there, I hope you will notice your feet, your hips, your belly and shoulders, your jaw, your eyes. Soften them now, please. Notice what happens in your body when you do, then your breath. Maybe you'll look now and see where you are. And when you see the impossible beauty of what is still alive outside, I hope you will weep tears of AWE for the gift of that. Both the seeing and the seen. This impossible "exito" (I say in Spanish, because the word reminds me of excitement, though it means achievement or accomplishment) of notes, sounds, entire symphonies that sing our lives into existence. I hope you'll weep and fall to the ground in reverence for the incredible gift of living here, in your body, on planet Earth.

In the heartbreak of loss we find the gift of the Western shield and its role in how we discover the true Self.

Ashwagandha - This amazing plant has been hailed for centuries in India as an Ayurvedic remedy for stress and resilience. The root and leaves are used to create a vitamin-like supplement that I have taken on and off for 20 years, and I am amazed at how much I endure, emotionally and physically. It is said to help balance blood sugar, balance hormones, and potentially fight cancer. Ashwagandha is a nightshade plant and therefore not to be used by those observing a nightshade-free diet.

Don't go outside your house to see flowers.

My friend, don't bother with that excursion.

Inside your body there are flowers.

That will do for a place to sit.

Sitting there you will have a glimpse of beauty

Inside the body and out of it,

before gardens and after gardens

~Kabir

PART II

FEEDING IN LAYERS AND CYCLES

CHAPTER SIX

UNTANGLING THE STRANDS OF NOURISHMENT

learning to feed

THE COSMOLOGY OF FEEDING

For me, Christianity got it right when it put the image of Mother Mary holding baby Jesus at the heart of its sacred symbolism. This relationship between mother and child is the root of Holiness. The way they feed each other nourishment, food, and love is the basic building block of all life. Only, the way I learned it, it was the relationship between Adam, Eve, an apple tree, and a serpent that laid the groundwork for the story of Creation in Christianity. Our entire Cosmology is based upon the betrayal of a male authority, God, and what happens when you "give into" temptation and eat what you we're told not to eat, in this case an apple. And so, we have been forever riddled by our own passions and our own drive toward physical embodiment, food, love, and life.

As Robin Wall Kimmerer asks in *Braiding Sweetgrass* (Milkweed Editions, 2013), what if we were given a different story of creation? What if we grew up feeding on stories where God, and Passionate Love, and the Fruiting Earth were all in harmonic resonance with how we celebrate and birth daily life, like the Tzutujil Cosmology Martin Prechtel describes in his books. There, in their creation story, we are one of the many layers of a fruiting tree whose roots are our ancestors, whose branches are our spiritual leaders/teachers, and whose fruits and flowers are the village people of *now*.

"Canyon Village understood the internal bigness of their world. Because every rock, trail, mountain, stump, spring, and incline was either the backbone of a dead giant in an old story, or a rock placed there by a Goddess who in her grief could go no farther, the land opened up in an internal immensity that was known only to the people whose world it was. The road map to this internal Tzutujil kingdom were the myriad of stories, mythologies, legends, and histories taught to them during ritual meetings and village initiations." (Martin Prechtel, *Long Life Honey in the Heart*)

The Tzutujil's life was a living form of Earth Reverence, woven into the mythic stories, the cosmology that they sang, spoke, ate, and fed daily to each other. Their beliefs about what held them in their deepest moments of loss and betrayal, grief and illness, were fertile, fecund, sexual, hungry, generous and, in turn, their lives were an embodied, living reflection of this.

My own personal experience has been that only when I finally adopted, lived, breathed, dreamed, and embodied this wild and fecund cosmology, did my own fertility "click" on. Just knowing that there is/was a people in my lifetime who, even in their language, birthed life daily through the ritual feeding of the spirits, that reflected their arduous daily task of feeding and harvesting the earth so they could survive, has been enough to transform my entire existence. As Prechtel describes it: "These (ritual) offerings kept the world alive, like the fertilizing and watering of a tree, an ancient tree that continuously bears the fruit of now." Everything is born into an active tense in the endless ritual of creating life.

The Ancient text of divination illuminates, once again, the importance of understanding relational dynamics and how they influence us:

I Ching #27 Nourishment

The symbol of Nourishment reminds us of an open mouth and appropriately calls us to nourish ourselves. Here, nourishment alludes to the feeding of all aspects of man's self: spiritual, emotional, and physical, and while suggesting the need to nourish self, may also be a call to feed or care for another. While food and drink nourish the heart and the body, the symbol of an open mouth also reminds us of the virtue embedded in our words. One is reminded to choose his words carefully. "A wise man moves his jaw with care. He does not risk injuring what is important for the sake of what is unimportant."

When ancient books of relational wisdom offer insights into what nourishment really is and accompany them with a symbol of an open mouth, I listen. I am always hungry for what is true.

ROOTS IN THE GROUND

This Reverence for life and the Earth that flowers and fruits in an endless cycle of exchange and beauty, a framework for how people lived in the past, is now a template for the future. It shows us how to interact, not just with the ground we walk on and the landscapes we live in, but with all of the things we harvest from that land, both literally and metaphorically.

There is so much confusion today around the simple question of what to eat. But if we look at food through the lens of reverence for the Earth and then food, the body of the Earth like your body, then we see it is meant to be taken in tides, in seasons, in ebbs and flows. Not because you are "on a diet" or "cleansing" or "detoxifying" or "sick" or "overweight," but because you are connected. Connected to where you are, to who you are, to how you feel, to what is actually growing outside, or not. Connected to space and time and seasonal cycles.

So, there is a time to empty and a time to fill. Not because you are religious, or spiritual, or healthy, or not healthy. But because you are paying attention. Because you are listening, moment to moment, every day, week, month, year, to what you really want and how different foods and their preparations impact you. You are listening because you appreciate all that happened in order to bring nourishment to you.

"When food is Love" —**Geneen Roth**

In Ayurveda, we say a meal is complete and will satisfy only when it has all of the flavors: bitter, sweet, astringent, salty, and pungent. We also look at foods that warm and those that cool, and we use those attributes to feed and balance one's internal and biological systems. Foods can be drying or moistening, detoxifying or restorative.

In Chinese Medicine, we see foods as pungent, sweet, sour, bitter, and salty, but more importantly as hot, warm, neutral, cool, and cold. This does not refer to the temperature they hold when you eat them, but a deeper internal heat or coldness that is essential to the food's nature and that will impact your internal chemistry.

In modern nutrition, we look at macro- and micro-nutrients including proteins, vitamins, minerals, calories, and fats. We talk about spicy and plain food. Raw or cooked. Instead of balancing the internal temperatures or attributes of the food, we seek to balance proteins with starches, fats, vitamins, and minerals.

In childhood and adolescence, our food needs are anabolic, seeking to build the body. Later, as more sedentary adults, we often need catabolic foods that break down fat and carry weight off of us, instead of putting it onto us.

Some say right diet depends on blood-type. Others, ancestry. Still others would offer macro-nutrient profiles as the most important quality to assess when deciding what to eat. You could say local, seasonal foods are the way to eat, or even say cooked or raw and hot or cold. That would depend on your current state of health and internal climate at the time. Further, you could consider organic or not organic, and wild or domesticated.

How we see food is driven today by science as much as culture. It is an analysis of parts, given to us by authorities who tell us they know better. We have come to believe so many things about food and feeding that I find are not even true. So here, we'll start again. And I start with an invitation to you. It is for you to start to pay attention, to ask: *what is true for me, now?*

There is too much information and too many decisions to be made if we look at food through a modern lens. But if we return to an idea of Reverence for Earth and the possibility of healing and growing in cycles, we harness the possibility of a deeper connection, both to ourselves and our intuition, that will guide us daily. In addition, connection to a culture, connection to a place, and connection to the nourishment of that place serves as a compass to keep us anchored and true. Within this connection it is easier to discern and determine what to eat and the way to eat, if you in fact have the choice. Not everybody does. Our choice is a privilege, and, as most people recognize, a responsibility.

How we choose to eat is our relationship to Earth, not just the earth (bone, muscle, organs) of our own bodies, but the planet that seeds, sprouts, grows, flowers, and fruits with us. So being aware of what we choose to support when we build our meals and put food in our mouths has an impact. It gives energy to what will live or what will not live. Yes, in the metaphysical sense, and also in what farmers choose to grow and how. What ranchers choose to do with their livestock and how. What international systems do with importing and exporting food stock and how. The choices you make of where to put your energy and what to put in your mouth reach long and far.

Plus, when feeding another such as your child, you are building the foundation of his/her body and his/her thoughts and beliefs about what is "good to eat."

If we are blessed, we can let go into the kitchen of a mother who was raised in an intact culture. A culture that still has roots in the ground. Her food and how she constructs it is intuitively right, balanced, and whole. Her cooking will intuitively combine the nutrients we need, as "traditional" food does. Unprocessed food inherently hosts the micro- and macro-nutrients we need to stay well.

Our options for what to eat are infinite. The only way to move ahead, though, is to look back. And to pay attention.

What sort of nourishment are you truly craving now?

THE HOME APOTHECARY

There are also so many forms of nourishment and ways to substitute and supplement, so many perspectives and entry points. From cultural frameworks to medicinal ones. Seasonal to scientific. I offer here my most distilled version. It's a simplification of all I have sifted through. These are the supplements that I have found to be safe, generally speaking, for our current realities of stress, adrenal fatigue, sleeplessness, and immune/endocrine/nervous system imbalance. Add Magnesium, Chlorella, Ashwagandha, and a Multi-mineral Supplement to your home apothecary for seasonal support. They address a broad spectrum of stress-related, modern conditions and offer ingredients that were once more ample in our food. These are simple tools, again, to consider in your regimen. They will not be effective for everyone all of the time. You, and your allies, have to be the judges.

"There are so many ways to be awake. There are so many names of God." —**The Book of Mastery**

Likewise, there are many forms of healing and many energy body maps. The ones illustrated here are my distillation of what I have seen and practiced across cultures and disciplines over the past 30 years. They may be called different names or approached with different languages or sensitivities, but the road maps are the same. These are maps and tools to empower your mind to remove blockages from your field, all the way down into your body.

But remember, a healthy relationship to food and nourishment also depends on your finding and embodying what makes your heart sing.

How is it that, even when people are starving, they can still be picky about what they eat?

Oliver went with his class to serve lunch at Glide Church in downtown San Francisco. "It was hard," he reported when he got home. "The smells, and seeing the people so unkept and unstable."

"I remember when we went with dad to serve lunch and that man fell asleep on top of his plate of food. When he woke up he started yelling that someone had taken his food," Rafa jumped in.

"Yeah, I remember," Oliver replied. "But what amazes me is that people who are starving, and have nothing, who are there for their first and only meal of the day, can be picky about what they eat! There are people there who refuse to eat things on their plates. I just don't get it."

This will remain here in question…

DOORWAYS TO DIGESTION

In Ayurveda, we say that good health and good digestion cannot be separated. How you receive and process food directly informs how well you are. This is true on a molecular level: how well your digestive systems can break down the nutrients in the food you eat and filter them on a cellular level into your blood, bones, organs, and other regulatory systems of your body. And on a spiritual level: how do you receive what you are given to feed from?

In Ayurveda we talk about *Agni*, the digestive fire. Strong digestive fire is considered an essential part of being well. It helps to digest and assimilate food into the body to build and maintain balance in and between the organ systems. Agni must be supported through food, herbs, and lifestyle.

Likewise, a healthy appetite and hunger, as we classify them in the West, are an essential ingredient for staying well. Instead of suppressing our appetites and limiting food intake, as many of us are taught to do, we could be celebrating them. We could be learning to recognize that a healthy appetite and ability to take in diverse foods supports our growth, our immunity, our endocrine system, and ultimately our relationship with the Earth.

Without proper digestion and assimilation we can't build the building blocks of the body and its diverse systems for maintaining health. This is understood across fields of medicine, from basic biology and Western Nutrition, to Ayurveda and Chinese Medicine. In Craniosacral therapy, we track the relationship between the nervous system and the body's ability to digest food or take in nourishment. There is a fundamental physiological relationship between one feeling safe and calm with one's ability to digest.

The simplest way to describe it is through the parasympathetic/sympathetic framework for the nervous system that is widely accepted as the biological model of how our nervous systems work. It suggests that we have two primary states of being: calm vs. activated. In the parasympathetic state where we feel safe, calm, and at ease, our organs function at their ultimate capacities. The lungs breathe, the heart circulates blood, the kidneys filter water and toxicity, the liver processes hormones and toxic substances, the spleen cleanses the blood, the stomach digests, and the intestines discern what to take in and what to eliminate. In this relaxed state, the digestive, immune, and endocrine systems are all at their best. So, the body's ability to digest anything, from emotional experience to food, is high.

On the contrary, if we don't feel safe, if there is any sense of perceived threat, and this can be either real or perceived, the body goes into a sympathetic response we call "fight or flight." Blood rushes from the core organs to the arms and legs to prepare for emergency, potentially a fight or an escape. So the organs' capacity to do their jobs decreases. Breath shortens, pulse or heart rate speeds up, and digestive and reproductive function either decrease or shut down all together. The body is in panic mode, and all systems organize around this. It's a basic biological response and a model that is accepted widely by the medical community. Most of us are living in some form of activation, from mild to acute, due to stored memories and external factors that agitate our nervous and immune systems constantly.

A newer model suggests that even before we move into the polarity of the Parasympathetic/Sympathetic model for the nervous system, or the calm and relaxed vs. the fight or flight mode, we have a social nervous system (Stephen Porges, *Polyvagal Theory,* 2002). It begins to show itself at infancy when a newborn looks to his/her mother's (or caregiver's) eyes to see if it's safe. A loud noise or sudden movement would suggest potential danger. The baby's first reaction is to seek eye contact. This is how it regulates and learns to feel safe, through eye contact and connection. Then, we see, it will seek comfort by latching on and eating. The baby, once it finds comfort and connection, begins to feed. Or it feeds to feel that connection and safety.

A baby's sense of self, of safety, of comfort, and of nourishment are all tied up in the experience of feeding at infancy. The baby's neural pathways that underlie his/her anatomy and biology are laid down here, now, in these earliest moments. The act of feeding, of connecting, of being protected and safe are all tightly woven together in the very beginning, as both exhibited in the process of early growth and development, and explained by the "Polyvagal Theory for the Nervous System" by Stephen Porges.

So, our earliest days are rooted in the development of the nervous system alongside the formation of the digestive system. The anatomy of our mouths, jaws, throats, stomachs, and the entire digestive system shapes itself throughout the intimacy of contact with mother during breastfeeding, folding the emotional cues and felt information into the biological development of the organs involved in feeding. The child is learning and forming, through mirroring the nervous system of the caregiver, its level of organization and security even before it drops into its own capacity to regulate.

It is our deepest and most basic anatomy:

how we feed

In addition to offering a socially driven explanation on the development and health of the nervous system and the other bodily functions that emanate from there, the Polyvagal Theory overturns our traditional belief that information is received first in the brain, and then from there transferred along neutral pathways into the body.

The wisdom resides in our body and in the structures of the nervous system that function outside the realm of awareness. In other words, cognitive evaluation… play(s) a secondary role to our visceral reactions to people and places." (Stephen Porges, *The Pocket Guide to the Polyvagal Theory: The Transformative Power of Feeling Safe*.) This idea supports contemporary research in Neuroception, the "process through which the nervous system evaluates risk without requiring awareness," and helps to build scientific frameworks for intuition and feelings in the gut or in the heart. Our visceral reactions to people and places are our first indication for survival: are you safe? You feel it in your gut.

THE NEW SCIENCE ON HOW WE FEED

This "new science" reframes older biological assumptions that we receive, gather, and process information in the brain. Information on safety can come literally straight to and from the gut, mobilizing a biological reaction even before the brain has time to process it. This reaction has the power to ignite a defensive response which immediately draws blood out of the core organs and into the limbs, thereby adjusting heart-rate, digestive capacity, and even immune and endocrine responses. So the Polyvagal Theory, while offering evidence for the psychophysiological development of our digestive or feeding mechanism, also creates and explanation for how feelings and emotions, as well as information in the field, impact an individual's biology and health. It also explains why feelings and feeding are so deeply intertwined. Then, it shows that if we don't feel safe, calm, or centered, our digestion is compromised. If our digestion is compromised, we cannot get the enzymes, energy, nutrients, and energetic components of food that our bodies need to thrive!

This is the Craniosacral perspective and why Craniosacral therapy can be so effective in working with newborns learning to latch on and feed. Or later in life with digestive challenges ranging from constipation, to stomach aches, to nervous tension and anxiety, to chronic gastrointestinal problems.

So when Alexei, now three years old, says to me "Mama, feed me!!" and refuses to eat without my sitting beside him or often even spoon feeding him, I am reminded of my own days with anorexia at age 13. I had trained myself so rigorously not to eat and to ignore my signals of hunger, desire, and fatigue, that when it came time to eat, now ordered by the doctor and others involved in my recovery, I was physically unable. I needed my mother to spoon feed me. I would wait in tears for her to get off of the phone and help me. Of course, neither of us understood what was going on. We just knew that this was so.

How do we teach our children to eat? I thought it would come naturally to them when they started eating food at age six months. They had been cared for in-utero and breast fed on demand since the day they were born. Now, wouldn't feeding come naturally and easefully? Yes, of course they would always prefer milk, but wouldn't they love all of these other offerings, coming into them without the cultural paradigms and frameworks that make eating hard for older children and adults. I thought so.

But I discovered all of my invisible and even unconscious thoughts about food surfacing in their responses to what was placed in front of them. And if I offered them something I did not embrace myself or did not fully connect with or wish to feed from myself, their willingness to feed was also reduced or absent.

What? How can this be? Do we pass these prejudices or closures on to our children? How? Can it be in our blood or DNA? Or is it an energetic transmission? How can my child be vegan? He's only two years old!?!? Given my cultural inheritance, I cannot fully embrace a diet free from dairy, eggs, or animal products for my babies! My adolescent perhaps, but not my babies. What will I possibly do?

My only relief came in the form of their fathers, stepping in with their unbridled appetites and desire to eat. The boys would immediately mirror their dads and begin to receive when before they would not. The walls of stone melted into their own mouths.

Our beliefs and ideas we have about food penetrate and permeate all that we eat. How we look at food impacts not only how our bodies will register what we eat, but how our children learn to feed. When we start to break apart "Earth Fruit" into constituent parts and analyze its nutritious constitution, we take the essence out of what is there to nourish us. Our minds begin to control what our bodies want and need. And, little by little, we give food POWER. The nourishment we are meant to feed from, to draw inspiration, energy, and a sense of connection and reverence from, begins to take power over us. It drives our minds and our behaviors into repetitive patterns and obsessive thoughts. Just this, the way our minds think about food and nourishment, takes us out of present time, essentially capturing the freedom of our Holy walk on the Earth. Like any addiction, our drive to have it/food/nourishment a certain way seizes our minds and robs us of our creative capacities to birth life in each moment.

How do we reclaim that power?

MEDICINE

"You are her medicine. Because you are embodied...at ease in your own flesh, your own appetites. Sensuous. Sexual. And offering yourself in that way. You're not seeking to control the things she has let define her life. So you are her remedy. It is her work to receive you. That is her medicine, what would make her better. And her impossible task."—Merrill Page

---

TRAUMA AND FOOD ALLERGIES

"I only sleep three to four hours a night," the Qigong Master told me in his broken and almost impossible to decipher English while he was drinking his Coca Cola and eating a bag of chips. But the point was clear, he hardly slept. Or so he said, and I believed him.

As a true master of Qigong, his laurels were praised and preached by many. Still, I had to see for myself just what this man was made of. So I signed up for his weekend workshop in Palm Beach Florida. The year was 1999.

Qigong was still new to me then and, like all energy practices, required my "Suspension of Disbelief." I was well-conditioned already in the practice of "suspending my disbelief," thanks to my love for Latin American Literature, its master Gabriel Garcia Marquez, and what Literature likes to call a genre: Magic Realism. And so, I knew how to allow things to unfold in their impossible beauty simply for the sake of the story and my own sense of hope. This phrase, "Suspension of Disbelief" is well-accepted in mainstream literature and is an excellent doorway into the principles of Energy Medicine.

So, I showed up for a class with a man whose language I didn't speak, with a group of people I'd never met, to spend the weekend following invisible energies through space, in impossible sequences I would never remember. At the end of each day, I did feel better though. Awake. Energized. Peaceful and renewed with hope.

What nobody told me was that, in March, in Florida, there are lice in the Ocean. They get trapped inside of your bathing suit and leave an itchy rash where they bite. Of course, I found myself covered in bites on Saturday after my swim. The itch was unbearable, but I went to class regardless. It was the day we were mapping points, energetic points connected to our organ systems, onto our backs. The teacher walked by as I was showing my partner my back and the rash from the sea lice. The teacher saw it and asked if it bothered me.

"Yes, it itches!" I told him emphatically.

"You want me to remove it?" he asked. I nodded.

So he had me lie face down on my stomach with my back bared, and in one instant he struck his finger from left to right, and right to left in an X motion over the rash. The itching let up immediately. It never came back. This was my initiation into Qigong.

Or was it mastery?

Or was it just what we can do with our energy?

Twenty-one years later I see it may have been my initiation into a lifetime of rashes and my extreme sensitivity to my surroundings. But beyond healing a rash with the sweep of his hand, what I was left with most was the control and impact this man had with both his mind and his body. And that he slept three to four hours a night and dined on cola and chips.

I think it was then, at age 24, that I also realized if your energy channels are open, clear, and resilient, it doesn't matter what you eat. He was an extreme example of this. It is the trauma of lived experience that shuts down the field of energy and inhibits digestion and assimilation. So, while food allergies, reactions, and rashes are complex and riddled with complications, there is this underlying aspect that often goes overlooked. The focus on food, limitation, and control of what we eat and don't eat has us chasing an impossible end and overlooking the root cause.

Resolving food allergies requires attention to what agitates the system and can be helped by removing the offender (that is, specific foods). But ultimately, allergies will be more fully addressed and resolved if we open the places in the body that are shut down or overwhelmed. Once the channels are open the body can more easily process the substances that agitate us.

Clearing trauma, however, and opening the energetic pathways of the body is not always an easy task, and few can do so with precision and mastery. Identifying and naming the trauma is the first impossible task. Is it a lived trauma, something that happened during the person's life that terrified or threatened them? Or was it a birth trauma, something that happened in-utero or during the birth and postpartum experience? More abstract even, and harder to identify, is the occurrence of trauma along the ancestral line, which, we see in Energy Medicine, gets passed down through generations into the lived experience of current family members. Research to show if it is passed through DNA or the blood or simply in the energetic fields is lacking, but as practitioners we witness bodily experiences of current generations living out ancestral patterns.[1]

The memory of trauma lives in the nervous system where, even if an offense seems minor to the rest of us, it can trigger a trauma reaction in an individual. This is what happens in PTSD, post-traumatic stress disorder, where an individual can be triggered by a stimulus that reminds him/her of the original traumatic experience. A system under such extreme stress, even if it is only "perceived stress," cannot possibly assimilate and digest all of the information coming into the system. The individual's nervous system is already overwhelmed and borrowing energy from the digestive, the reproductive, and the endocrine systems to address immediate survival needs. Food then, and its many molecular components, is one more complication. And so, I associate food allergies and other allergies with unresolved trauma.

Donna Eden has tracked food allergies and other sensitivities to seemingly benign substances such as dust, to the original traumatic event. She says when a substance such as dust or grass pollen is present during a specific overwhelming episode, it may likely show up later as an allergy.[2] Our bodies lose the motility to assimilate and digest basic substances when they are in extreme survival situations.

How do we begin to resolve the trauma then?

It requires the partnership of a good practitioner with the client. Someone who is experienced in the field of one of the diverse forms of Energy Medicine, including Therapeutic Touch, Medical Qigong, Polarity therapy, Acupuncture, Somatic therapy, Touch for Health, or Intuitive Medicine, can initiate an opening that supports the release of traumatic memories from your bodymind. Then, to maintain the new opening, the client must participate. There are exercises we can do to support and protect our body and the fields around them to prevent falling back into these "allergic" reactions or sensitivities.

AN EXERCISE TO RE-PATTERN THE NERVOUS SYSTEM

The Nervous Systems can be treated and re-patterned through touching into the cranial nerves. There are 12 of them, each with a specific pathway and assignment. A good Craniosacral practitioner is well-versed in all of them and knows each one's function, pathway, and access points.

One of these 12 nerves is the optic nerve, and it controls the eyes. Sometimes just softening the eyes is enough to shift the system from a hyper-vigilant state to a relaxed state. This in itself is strong medicine and can be enough to enhance digestive function and restore a healthier endocrine balance, especially if practiced regularly over time.

Eye Pattern Release - The movement of your eyes is directly linked to the function of your nervous system. Simple exercises, such as relaxing your eyes, can have a profound effect throughout your entire body. More specific exercises, such as moving your eyes from left to right across the center/mid-line of your body, can also facilitate integration of seen and felt experience into your body in a healthy way.

Here is an exercise you can practice to restore balance to a body that is triggered by difficult memories. Deepak Chopra, a leading MD in the field of Ayurveda, mind-body science, and how we apply physics to medicine, taught me this one.

I.

Sit in a chair, legs uncrossed, feet placed hip width apart flat on the floor, and bring your attention to your feet.

Imagine your feet letting go down into the ground

Bring your attention to your eyes, soften them

Soften your:

> jaw
> shoulders
> lower back
> thighs

Imagine letting them all go down into the ground

Move your eyes left and right, from side to side as far as they will go, across the midline of your body.

Rotate them back and forth looking up, toward the top of your head, left to right. 10 to 20 times.

Then center, side to side, left to right. 10 to 20 times.

Then down, toward the ground, left to right across the midline. 10 to 20 times.

Pause. Notice how you feel.

Take three deep breaths in and out and close your meditation.

Practice daily.

II.

Sit in a chair, legs uncrossed, feet placed hip width apart flat on the floor, and bring your attention to your feet.

Imagine your feet letting go down into the ground

Bring your attention to your eyes, soften them

Soften your:

> jaw
> shoulders
> lower back
> thighs

Imagine letting them all go down into the ground

Place your hand in front of the center of your brow known as the third eye, with your fingers pressed together pointing toward you. (Practice with both your dominant and non-dominant hands, as each hand influences the wiring in your nervous system differently.)

Draw a figure 8 with your hand, cycling from side to side to the edge of your forehead with its center point at your third eye. Allow your eyes to follow.

If it's comfortable, allow yourself to bring up the memory of a charged experience.

Remember it as you cycle your eyes from left to right.

Consider working with a trusted friend and ally when you do this, as it can be a strong experience.

Food, once an easy entry into the sensual and grounded body, has become as complex and riddled as the minds who have made it what it is today. So much of what we eat we must buy at the store, so we have no connection to it. The implications of this practice are showing up in so many ways that we almost cannot track them anymore. From obesity to compromised immunity, from depression and lethargy to hyperactivity, from irritable bowel syndrome to chronic digestive problems, all can find relief in cultivating and caring for a connection to our food. The solution, as multifaceted as the problem, will come in a re-claiming of old ways. It will require a shift in our beliefs, an adjustment in our behaviors, an adaptation in our food production and consumption, and an expansion in how we perceive who we are and how we nourish.

NOTES

CHAPTER SEVEN

FOOD:

MAPPING A NEW REALITY

in search of truth

Since food and nourishment are so embedded in culture and beliefs, the only way to change how we eat and how we are nourished is to change how we think about food. What is true? What is not? Below are the maps of a new doorway into how you perceive and relate to food. I invite you to sink a little deeper into receptivity and notice the qualities of each morsel you bring into your body. Your perception, together with these pieces of information, will light the way.

DANCING IN THE MIRROR OF THE SEASONS

The essence of **Winter** is slow and still, so the foods we use to heal need to mirror this. Warm, cooked foods with protein are good choices to soothe the digestive system and the nervous system and promote sound sleep and restoration. Good fats, like Olive Oil, Sunflower Oil, Flax Oil, Sesame Oil, Almond Oil, and Coconut Oil, find their place here in winter, and we can even use Sesame Oil to massage the skin. It is deeply hydrating and calming. In winter, many of us are bound indoors and less active. So it makes sense to decrease the amounts of carbohydrates, grains, and sugars we consume.

Choose soups, stews, roasts, leafy greens, winter fruits like pears, apples, pomegranates, oranges, grapefruit, lemons. Oatmeal cooked in water with flax oil and dried fruit is warm and soothing at breakfast. A pureed carrot or squash soup with a crusty fresh bread or brown rice tortilla can be a satisfying lunch. Corn tortillas with pulled meats of choice, avocado, fresh onion (to fend off winter bugs), and salsa is a simple, hearty dinner in the Winter.

The essence of **Spring** is faster. There's an excitement in the air as the earth comes back to life, and we feel this in our bodies. The green sprouts and dandelions peeking out from the ground are singing a new form of life and begging for us to listen. One way to wake up from the slower slumber of winter is to EAT these foods. The sprouts, the bitter greens, or the onions and lettuces in the store if you don't live where you see them outside. Our bodies, like an Earth ecosystem, are shifting from the freeze to burbling creeks. It's wet, and we are wise to balance this dampness with a drier diet. Reducing oils and fats, cutting back on protein, and introducing grains back into the diet is a natural way to do this.

Choose puffed cereal in the morning such as millet, amaranth, kamut. Eat salads instead of soups for lunch with spring fruit, even dried such as dates, figs, plum, apple, pineapple, raisins, cranberries, and cherries. Dinner can be cooler and lighter, such as grilled meat with asparagus, instead of that chicken soup or beef stew.

The essence of **Summer** is the fastest, and our diets should naturally mirror this. Unlike the slower meals of winter, we might eat more little things on the go—fruit, raw vegetables, fresh juices, or waters can even take the place of a full meal. When your appetite is full and hearty, you can eat food that is cooked more quickly, like seared fish with rice and vegetables or leafy greens with protein. The fire of digestion allows you to assimilate raw food more easily than in the cold winter months. And the aliveness of the food will carry you without the dense calorie-loading more appropriate to winter.

Choose cherries for breakfast! With nectarines, peaches, plums, pluots, or other seasonal fruit. If your appetite is strong, add fruit to a bowl with yogurt or oat or rice milk, oats, puffed millet, ground flax, or other cereals. For lunch eat fresh greens, cold salads of chicken or meats, whole grain breads with nut spreads, jam or honey, and sprouts on top. Dinner can be beet salad, or lentil salad, or potatoes boiled, cooled, and tossed with celery, olive oil, and lemon. Gazpachos are also good options, with a piece of grilled fish, meat, or vegetable.

Fall starts to slow us down again. At least this is its intention. You can see it and feel it in the light, if you pay close attention. How we eat and how we prepare foods needs to shift now, too. It is time to go back to a slower way of cooking, such as roasting or stove-top cooking, rather than raw or seared foods. The fruits offered up in nature transition from stone fruits such as peaches, nectarines, and plums, and to apples and pears. It is medicine to make this shift, as it is happening around us. To make new choices in food, and thereby stay connected to the true local offerings. It is also how we keep our dishes simple.

So choose apples, pears, oranges as they come available. Shift from yogurt, which the fires of summer allowed you to digest with more ease, back to cooked grains such as rice congees for breakfast. Toast with nut-butters may work for you, too. Lunch favors more and more cooked foods if you like them. Salads done with local greens fruits and vegetables can also work. Pickled, alive vegetables such as sauerkrauts and onions also support health of the fall season. They are wonderful on top of any dish, including raw salads or cooked grains with vegetables or proteins.

We eat this way to make music, something your body can feed from, that inspires the heart, inspires movement, inspires connection, and hopefully *play*. The elements combine according to the principles of balance in any living ecosystem or life system. When food comes into you in the right way, it is like a set of good musical instruments creating harmony inside of you. It is an interplay of notes that simultaneously feed your spiritual/emotional/physical bodies. That is, your cells, your nervous system, your endocrine system, your fluid blood system, your immune system, and beyond. Not because you thought about it or analyzed it, controlled, restricted, or designed it, or even understood or rationalized. But because you were open, willing, and able to receive.

FOOD COMBINING FOR BETTER DIGESTION

One step toward taking back your power from food is understanding how it works inside of you. Gas, bloating, belching, discomfort, and sluggishness after eating as well as constipation, diarrhea, or apathy around food can often be improved by more careful selection of which foods you eat together. This is both a modern concept, driven by doctors of nutrition and dietary studies, and an ancient one, passed along through Ayurveda and Chinese Medicine.

Other earth-based systems of healing—where food was carefully combined to mirror seasonal offerings, where cultural education was offered around what worked together and what didn't, and where food combinations were still carefully guarded and passed along—also respect these principles of eating certain foods together and others all alone.

"If you eat poetry for breakfast, it balances your blood chemistry." —**Megan Goulder, Bodyworker (Instagram post)**

I have been playing with these ideas for 33 years now, and I have found tremendous relief and ease with some basic principles in food combining and seasonal eating. Here is what I have found to be true:

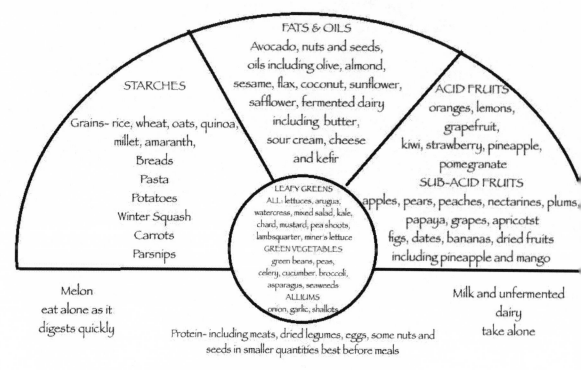

FATS & OILS
Avocado, nuts and seeds,
oils including olive, almond,
sesame, flax, coconut, sunflower,
safflower, fermented dairy
including butter,
sour cream, cheese
and kefir

STARCHES

Grains- rice, wheat, oats, quinoa,
millet, amaranth,
Breads
Pasta
Potatoes
Winter Squash
Carrots
Parsnips

ACID FRUITS
oranges, lemons,
grapefruit,
kiwi, strawberry, pineapple,
pomegranate

SUB-ACID FRUITS
apples, pears, peaches, nectarines, plums,
papaya, grapes, apricotst
figs, dates, bananas, dried fruits
including pineapple and mango

LEAFY GREENS
ALL: lettuces, arugua,
watercress, mixed salad, kale,
chard, mustard, pea shoots,
lambsquarter, miner's lettuce
GREEN VEGETABLES
green beans, peas,
celery, cucumber, broccoli,
asparagus, seaweeds
ALLIUMS
onion, garlic, shallots

Melon
eat alone as it
digests quickly

Milk and unfermented
dairy
take alone

Protein- including meats, dried legumes, eggs, some nuts and
seeds in smaller quantities best before meals

FOOD COMBINING TO IMPROVE DIGESTION

A MUSICAL TOUR OF GREENS AND THEIR NOTES

In addition to being a delightful experience, and creating a sense of joy when you eat them, greens have incredible, diverse, and profound health benefits. Dr. Elson Haas, author of *Staying Healthy with the Seasons* (Celestial Arts, 1981) and a leader in the field of integrating Western Medicine with Eastern health philosophies and science writes, "the active part of these plants, giving them their green color, is chlorophyll, which may be one of the strongest true healing agents known to man."

Chlorophyll is almost bio-identical to hemoglobin, the molecule in blood that transports oxygen throughout your body. As such, it has an amazing capacity for cleansing, purifying, and restoring the blood. Since 1950, even the medical community has recognized chlorophyll's power to heal wounds, ulcers, and inflammation in the digestive tract.

Greens, despite their lightness and categorization in the vegetable kingdom, offer bio-available protein in the form of minerals that support both the nervous and the endocrine system, acting as enzymes to activate neurotransmitters. And they are loaded with essential vitamins.

Greens play a role in cleansing the liver, which supports the entire body in its function of balancing and eliminating hormones, toxins, and waste. Having a healthy liver is a foundational piece in keeping the body balanced and well.

According to Anthony William, leafy greens also support the alkalinity of the lymphatic system, which is, though unknown to the medical community, responsible for keeping the blood, organs, endocrine, reproductive, and nervous systems alkaline (Anthony William, *Foods that Heal*). The state of alkalinity in the body ultimately supports health by boosting the immune system and keeping bacteria, viruses, molds, and fungi in balance.

Finally, green food, being the color of the heart chakra, would support heart function on its spiritual emotional level. In Chinese Medicine, we say that the health of the heart is the cornerstone for health in the entire mindbody.

Arugula - Arugula, a hearty dark and usually spicy green, grows happily in warm and cold. Thus, you'll find it in the garden and in season through the fall, winter, spring, and into summer again. It is cleansing and rich in minerals, including iron. I eat it for breakfast as the seasons change in the fall, with a tart apple and something starchy.

Bibb - Bibb lettuce is light green and holds more water and neutrality than a neighbor like arugula. It is hydrating and a wonderful base for a summer salad. Because of its neutrality, it is also a good background for cheeses, including sharp or salty ones like Jarlsberg or Parmesan.

Boston Lettuce - Boston serves as a wonderful backdrop or canvas for other bold flavors, offering hydration and minerals to a meal and a light-hearted, gluten-free way to wrap your meal. It is high in silicon, which assists in absorption of calcium in the bones.

Butter Lettuce - Includes both Bibb and Boston lettuces, known for their light color and wide flowering leaves. It is described as sweet and mild on the spectrum of leafy greens and does well with creamy dressings or behind other summer flavors such as peaches, cherries, or even cheese.

Cilantro - The true power of cilantro comes through in its robust and unequivocal flavor. Tossed as an herb into a salad, it has the power to shape your entire experience. I used to say it tastes like bad breath, which, I have been told, means that I was in particular need of its healing agents. It detoxifies not just the blood, but also on a cellular level, reaching into the deepest places of our bodies to remove both physical and psychic residue. It also serves as a beautiful way to cool hot and spicy flavors and to balance fat, hence its essential role in Central American cuisine.

Dandelion - The dandelion is famous in the spring for invading open space and well-kept lawns or gardens. Its perseverance shows me its strength and devotion as a medicinal plant with a power akin to the liver, whom it most directly speaks to. Its bitterness is its strength and, added to a salad, it offers the healing property of being cleansing/detoxifying. It balances and clears excess or unwanted fat from the system and offers us a fresh take on spring.

Escarole - Escarole could be perhaps mistaken for a butter lettuce in its color and shape, but its leaves have a sharp edge, like a holly leaf, and its shape is taller and narrower than a head of Bibb or Boston. Known in Italian kitchens as mainly a cooked green, steamed then squeezed before it's added to a searing pan with olive oil and garlic, I find I prefer it raw in salads. Like butter lettuces, it is deeply hydrating, but much more bitter and slightly astringent. It shows itself strongly in the winter and balances beautifully the heavier winter foods such as stew, both in taste and its energetic properties.

Frisee - Frisee is the edgy, thin leaf I used to pick out of my salads and toss to the side. I said it scratched my throat and irritated my mouth, compared to its gentler cousins called red and green leaf lettuces or spring greens. Now, I reach for a head of frisee when I see it in the store and rush home to soak and rinse it, then make a salad of frisee alone. Its spindly shape holds its bitterness with an extra edge, proving again that form is function. Its function is also to clear and cleanse and, with a cooked meat or dark stew, it serves the purpose of balancing a meal and helping you to digest fats.

Kale - The superhero of modern greens, kale is found in diverse forms including dinosaur kale (also called Tuscan Kale) and curly kale we commonly find at the grocery store. Its dark green color translates to its taste, which is rich in green and iron, and its season, which is winter. Since it is robust throughout the year, it can be cooked in winter, simmered, seared, and even eaten raw. When eating raw, choose tender baby greens, or chop and massage the larger leaves with olive oil, salt, and lemon to improve digestibility. The mature leaves can also be roasted for chips that even children love. Peel off stem, massage with olive oil and a dash of salt, and roast at 425° for some 15 minutes until brown and crisp.

Lambsquarter - Lambsquarter, though delicate and unassuming, has the perseverance of a dandelion that makes me believe it is medicinal. It grows like a weed between your chosen crops and, like purslane, is often torn out and discarded. All undomesticated plants, however, have a unique energy that cultivated plants do not. Their wild spirits are still intact, which is why I choose to center them in my bowls.

Mint - Like cilantro, mint's presence and power announces itself through its unique and distinct flavor. Edible mint, like most of our edibles, comes in variations from spearmint to peppermint and can be added as an uplifting surprise to a salad or spring roll. It cools and refreshes, awakens the mind, and calms the tummy. It is believed to hold enough power to even neutralize homeopathic remedies and should therefore be avoided in all forms, including toothpaste, when one is taking homeopathic orally.

Mustard Greens - Young mustard greens can light up a salad and steal the show, if you like heat in your bowl. Dark, spicy, and alive, they add a peppery character to a sometimes bland bowl of mixed greens. When allowed to develop fully, they concentrate their heat and spiciness and can wrap easily around a handful of rice for a snack or mid-day gluten-free, everything-free but flavorful meal.

Parsley - Parsley, once tossed aside as a green garnish on an otherwise edible plate, is the center point of many of our meals. Not only does it embody the taste of green and minerals, but it is also filled with them. It is a storehouse of micro-minerals that serve as essential enzymes in the health maintenance of the body, and it gives us the vibration of green in our cells, the truest kind of food to support both the liver and the heart. Blended up with green apple, olive oil, lemon, and cayenne, it can be poured on any dish, hot or cold, to tie together diverse or bland flavors and make your meal, and your body, sing.

Purslane - The first time I encountered purslane it was as a mat of tangled weeds covering my front garden in my new little home in New Mexico. My mother, an East Coaster, and an experienced and sophisticated gardener, told me it was invasive, a weed, and to get it out. Then, the gardener at the local nursery of Indigenous plants told me I could eat it. So, it stayed. At least for a moment. What the gardener didn't tell me is that it is much better in a bowl of other mixed greens, not alone. Purslane looks and tastes like a succulent plant, holding water in both its leaf and stem. It is a combination of red and green and, again, its weed-like insistence makes me confident of its medicinal abilities.

Radicchio - Just the thought of radicchio makes my mouth pucker. Its brilliant bitterness and astringency builds out a bowl of greens into something more sophisticated. European. My sister taught me that butter lettuces need radicchio to make them even worth eating. Then, seeing, holding, smelling, and bringing home my first whole head of radicchio taught me I need radicchio, its compact shape and form, its deep purple color, its modest presence on a shelf at the store, to feel my own depth, humility, and heart.

Watercress - The peppery spice of watercress delights and excites me every time I taste it. It pops in my mouth, announcing its unique presence and medicinal properties. It seems to say "I am green! I will feed you, cleanse your blood, and restore your body," just like the creeks or streams it grows in that feed and cleanse their local landscapes. Watercress in particular is known for being a blood builder and is excellent in cases where one supplements or seeks out non-animal sources of iron.

FAT IS GOOD

Fat has long been a controversial topic. "Shhhh!" I whisper, when my child points and says, "Look how fat he/she is." Equally, we judge food when we see it laced with fat and seek out options that call themselves "fat free" or "low fat." While the news has broken, FAT IS NOT BAD and NOT ALL FATS ARE CREATED EQUAL, there is still a lot to be learned and understood about how they are different and where the different fat options belong.

In our house, I trim the fat off of the meat and skim fat off of the soup stock when it cools. I refuse to cook with butter, and I don't like cooked cheese on any food. But you will find me putting thick layers of Earth's Balance on my tortillas, eating cheese raw, and buying whole milk yogurt in the winter. Our rice bowls are drenched in flax oil, I seek out salmon and cold water fish in the market, and we eat cakes made with one cup of olive oil to two cups of flour. Eggs are cooked in thick layers of mixed olive and sunflower oil, and we do love whipped cream on our ice cream.

Like all things, fats require discernment. Their season is when we are building, either in pregnancy or after birth, growing as a child into an adult, or in fall and winter. They can be used to restore in times of depletion or protect when one is cold or physically or emotionally vulnerable. More dietary fat is even recommended for thinner body types who tend to run dry or be nervous. The fats serve to ground, stabilize, and nourish.

Fats provide energy, insulation, and the means for absorbing Vitamins A, D, E, and K. Lipids, the name for the fat compound in both food and in our bodies, are an essential component in every cell wall/membrane, including your brain, your organs, your skin, and your nervous system. They help to protect, to facilitate the communication of information across a cell wall, and to assimilate critical vitamins such as Vitamin D. In addition, lipids play a key role in the formation and function of both hormones in the endocrine system and eicosanoids, a hormone-like substance that helps regulate blood pressure, blood clot formation, and healthy blood. Eicosanoids are also essential in the body's immune response to an injury or an infection.

In addition, fat serves an emotional need: it is calming. As such, it is a key player in healthy functioning of your nervous system. The balance of one's body, the ability to function and grow, digest, and reproduce, sleep and be productive, depends on it. All of us are supported by the protective and grounding attributes of fats.

Essential Fatty Acids are the most critical for us to consume in our diets and are found in nuts and seeds, mother's milk, some micro-algae, cold-water fish, and many grains, legumes, fruits, and meats. Also known as Omega-3 and Omega-6 fats, their function in the body, through the biological conversion into prostaglandins, help to regulate every cell and organ in the body. From the activation of the T-cells in the immune system, to the regulation of the nerves, and the maintenance of the cardiovascular system, to the production of hormones from insulin to estrogen, and the production of healthy skin and hair, all benefit from dietary intake of essential fatty acids. (Paul Pitchford, *Healing with Whole Foods*)

EAT FAT. BUT HOW AND WHEN?

The best kind of dietary fat is the kind that nourishes and supports formation of the cell wall, our immune system, nervous system, cardiovascular system, and endocrine system without leaving fat deposits in our blood vessels or organs. This requires attention to the balance of fats, carbohydrates, and sugars coming into the body through food and can be controversial in how one achieves balance. Research, however, scientifically reveals the danger of too much animal fat or dairy fat in the diet and also foods that provide too much cholesterol. It also asserts the importance of Essential Fatty Acids, Omega-3 and Omega-6, for helping to balance good and bad cholesterol throughout the body and perform all of the necessary functions that fat does, including providing 60% of our energy when we are at rest (Whitney and Rolfes, *Understanding Nutrition*).

Below is my list of favorite fats, in addition to the nuts, seeds, legumes, leafy vegetables, fish, and milk that carry them.

Micro-algae - chlorella, spirulina, and wild blue-green algae are three examples of micro-algaes and excellent ways to nourish your self. In addition to providing protein and micronutrients, they have added elements to detoxify, purify, and restore the blood. Then, they offer a balanced profile of healthy fats that are easily assimilated into the body. I like mine in tiny tablets first thing in the morning or with orange juice as a snack in the afternoon (the Vitamin C from the OJ helps me absorb the iron in my chosen micro-algae: chlorella). Remi likes his blended into a milky drink made with one of the many milks listed below, frozen banana, papaya, dates, blueberries, etc.

Flax Oil - My senior project as an undergrad at Stanford University was to help a graduate student assemble all of the clinical studies and research that had EVER been done on one plant: Flax. It wasn't until 15 years later that ground flax appeared as a regular item on the shelf of a mainstream grocery store such as Trader Joe's and Whole Foods. This beautiful, whimsical blue flower produces a seed that can be consumed as an oil, ground, or even whole. It provides a nutritional profile of Omega-3 and Omega-6 fats believed to match the potency of cold water fish. These are the fats that balance hormones and restore cell walls and overall cell function. We all adore flax oil on our rice and greens, and many people put it in smoothies. Flax is to be used cold and raw. Heat destroys it.

Olive Oil - The Mediterranean Diet and its reputation for healthy living is a true testimony to the therapeutic and delicious qualities of this oil. It is an excellent choice both in cooking and eating raw as it retains its composition well at high heat. It is an antioxidant, by nature, helping to keep you healthy while nourishing your hair, skin, nails, and cell walls.

Sesame Oil - In addition to simply being rich in flavor and nourishing, sesame oil is high in unsaturated fat and in essential fatty acids, making it an ideal choice for the diet. It is high in antioxidants, which supports the immune system and protects the heart. And it is anti-inflammatory, offering support in healing and recovery from inflammation, both internal and external.

Sunflower Oil (oleic) - The seeds of the sunflower offer a most natural and abundant source of a beautifully composed fat. It is an unrefined monounsaturated fat which means you can cook with it, and it has a good price point.

Note: When meals or their ingredients aren't "just right" and something is too fatty, we can bring it to balance with another ingredient like marmalade with cheese or parsley and cilantro on a stew meat or rich soup. The Guatemalan's also taught me that a squeeze of lime cuts the fat in a good bone broth.

MILK

I love milk. It is a resting place for me. Something I turn to for comfort, nourishment, a sense of completion and ease. But, I don't drink it, not any more at least.

Milk is controversial. Is it healthy? Is it not? Does it build your bones and supply your body with needed calcium and Vitamin D, or does it strip them of the nutrients you need to grow or maintain a beautiful body? There is research to argue both sides, and too much money has been spent doing so. Then, there is the reality of how raising cattle for milk impacts a local ecosystem and other potential uses for it. Or, how humane is the treatment of the cows whose milk we take to feed us, instead of their young?

The possibilities for how we perceive and receive milk are unending. And so, we have played with all of them. One of my favorite moments was recognizing that we had five different kinds of milk on average, in our fridge, when my boys were babies. They ranged from Mother's milk to cow's milk, from almond to soy, and from rice to goat's milk. In time, I have acquired allergies to the soy and the almond milk, sensitivity and intolerance to the lactose in the cow's milk, and a skin reaction/allergy to oat milk. So my search for that creamy connection that comes with drinking milk, and how it registers so deeply in my library of memories on nourishment, continues. Here are some milk profiles to help you find your own way. Many of the micronutrient benefits aren't measured on the boxes, and you can look into those as you choose. I have selected the macronutrient profiles that most direct my decisions.

NO MORE MOTHER'S MILK

Type	Calories/cup	Sugars	Protein
Almond	40	1	1
Almond milk, an all-time favorite of mine, is earthy and anchored, and offers the cold, creamy refreshment of a milky drink without too much sugar or nuttiness.			
Cashew	50	0	1
Cashew milk is rich and deep, offering a buttery flavor that some like in their milks, with a little protein and no sugar.			

Coconut	80	0	.5
Coconut milk is creamy, rich, and loaded with healthy minerals and good fats. It is considered a nut, so if you are allergic to nuts, feel your way. It may not be the choice for you.			
Flax	25	0	0
Flax milk is a balanced option, low in calories, hypo-allergenic for those allergic to soy or nuts, and high in quality fats including Omega 3 and 6. The flavor is appealing and somewhat neutral but reminiscent of the taste of flax seeds.			
Hazelnut	90	1	2
Hazelnut milk is not found on the grocery shelves where I live, but it can be made at home with a recipe listed below. Like all nut milks, it offers the subtle flavor of its ingredients with a creamy depth that leaves a milk-lover feeling settled and complete.			
Hemp	60	0	3
Hemp milk is slightly nutty and loaded with body. It is a great option for those avoiding soy or nuts, as it is hypo-allergenic and offers a balanced nutritional profile.			
Macadamia	50	0	1
Macadamia nut milk is gaining popularity for its nutritional benefits. Buttery and round in flavor, it also is high in omega fats and low in carbs.			
Oat	45	2	1
Oat milk was a favorite of mine until my body reached its tipping point in my dust allergy (dust can accumulate in processed oats). Oats again are a great alternative to soy and nuts, and the milk is creamy, deep, balanced, and delicious.			
Rice	120	11	0
Rice milk has won my heart for its ability to hold coldness, the way oats hold heat on a cold morning. So it is refreshing, slightly sweet, ice cold, and tastes simple. I find it ungrounding on its own and perhaps too simple to meet a milk craving, so I like to mix it with flax or hemp milk to ground it and give it depth.			
Soy	80	1	7
Soy milk has a slightly bean'y flavor and a good structure with depth and complexity that makes it a good alternative to milk. Soy, however, can produce allergic reactions and may be too high in estrogens to benefit growing boys. Something to consider. There is also controversy on whether un-sprouted soy, though high in protein, is beneficial to the human digestive system.			
Walnut	120	0	3
Walnuts are excellent brain food, as their shape suggests, and offer wonderful forms of fat for the nervous system and healthy cells. Though not readily available in most health stores, walnut milk is something you can make at home.			

Goat's	170	11	9
Goat's milk, if it appeals to your pallet, is a great alternative to cows. It doesn't produce the same reaction to lactose as cow's milk, so it is not as likely to give you cramps and gas. And raising goats for milk is ecologically less devastating than cows.			
Raw	150	12	8
Raw milk is believed to be superior to standard or organic milk due to the pre- and probiotics it contains. So, it has the beneficial bacteria to help support and sustain a healthy "micro-biome" or gut. A healthy gut ultimately protects the health of all of your body systems.			
Organic 2%	25	12	8
Organic Milk is beneficial not only to your body, as it doesn't have the pesticide and toxic chemicals found in non-organics, but also to the ecosystem where the cows who give this milk are raised. Since care is taken to maintain a healthy balance of natural elements in the local habitat of these cows, everything feeding and living there has a stronger chance at health across spectrums.			
Standard 2%	125	12	8
The benefits of drinking cow's milk today are controversial. For children, it can offer a shortcut to complete nourishment. In a healthy ecosystem, where the milk is local and clean and the child's digestive system is balanced and receptive, it can be an ideal food. Unfortunately, many of our local environments no longer reflect this level of purity or concern in food production from the ground up, so milk can hold microscopic levels of toxic chemicals and other byproducts of production that, over time, may contribute to compromised immunity or endocrine imbalance.			

Oat Milk - *another good alternative to milk, soy milk, or nut milks. Great for those with lactose intolerance or nut/soy allergies. Offered now at many stores, but you can also make your own, in the interest of self-sufficiency and reducing waste. This way you can also adjust taste with vanilla or maple syrup, if you prefer.*

1/3 to 1/2 cup oats (whole, but not steal cut)
Pinch of sea salt
approx. 3 cups water

Combine in blender, and blend until smooth. Pour into cloth strainer bag and squeeze 'til milk comes out, leaving oats in bag. (I set up a sauce pan with a strainer and do it into this, then pour into a glass milk pitcher of choice). Chill and enjoy.

Almond Milk - *almonds are strong, hearty, resilient, and blessed with a fragrance reminiscent of a delicate cherry blossom in the spring. You can taste it in their essence. When I gave up cow's milk, I sought the balance of almonds: almond milk, almond cream cheese, almond butter and flour. Now, I am allergic to them! Note to self:* "Addiction, to anything, means one day you may have to give it up. Walk lightly and remember to breathe."

> *1/3 cup raw almonds*
> *Pinch of sea salt*
> *Approx. 3 cups water*

Combine in blender, and blend until smooth. Pour into cloth strainer bag and squeeze 'til milk comes out, leaving oats in bag. (I set up a saucepan with a strainer and do it into this, then pour into a glass milk pitcher of choice). Chill and enjoy.

 **"All is Well"** (**to practice before you eat**) - *What happens when we say these words? There is the possibility of whatever burden you are carrying to lift up or be set down. The weight on your shoulders falls away, and you can savor the simplicity of being ok, now, in this moment. It is a basic but profound concept, and it comes in the statement of three words. Three words, like I love you, or you delight me, or life is good. These are the thoughts I want you to bring to the table. Come, sit now. Let it all go down into the ground. Here are three steps to prepare you to eat. Practice them each time you feed, whether you sit down at a table, or not.*

Feel your feet

Notice your breath

Soften your eyes

Only then, once you're in intimate contact with your body, begin to eat.

Digestive Enzymes - when life serves up something other than ideal seasonal food prepared just right; or a stress-free day, month, year; or you eat more than you really needed to eat, then digestive enzymes are a wonderful ally. They are enzymatic formulas that combine the ingredients you need to help digest your meal, including amylase for carbohydrates, protease for protein, and lipase for fats. You take one to two pills or capsules following a meal to speed up digestion and help your body assimilate the nutrition in the food. You can find them at most health food stores or online. Not all are created equal, so pay attention. If it's not working, try again.

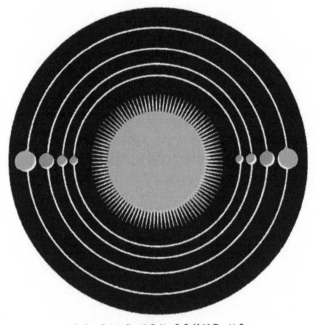

SO GLAD YOU FOUND ME

CHAPTER EIGHT

BODY ENERGY

CHAPTER EIGHT

reworking reality from a fluid model

Beyond the formation of your body, there is the formation of your being. Just like the Earth has many layers inward into the core and outward into the stratosphere, you are layered, more densely as we move inward and more subtly as we move outward into the field beyond your body. Earth Medicine must address you in this same manner, with the understanding of your subtle bodies. Just like healing the Earth requires attention to multidimensional health including air, earth, water, ether, and fire, your well-being requires attention to each element of you. Your health must be addressed this way, with attention to the balance within and between each element as it manifests in you.

ANTHROPOSOPHY AND AYURVEDA

Systems of medicine across the ages have mapped out subtle bodies, linked them to natural elements, and proposed ways of meeting them or treating them. Different cultures have mapped different layers and found different points for entering and exiting them. In Ayurveda and yogic practices for example, we look at the chakra centers along the north-south pole of the body as the doorways in and out of the body and as the main energy centers for treating disease. In Chinese Medicine, we track points along many more channels on the surface of the skin and treat even deep illness through them. In Polarity therapy, we can access imbalances through different body maps and, for example, can even touch into the fire element through an energetic channel in the second toe, thereby restoring healthy digestive function and other ailments associated with fire imbalance. In Craniosacral therapy, we contact the energetic and physical bodies simultaneously through contacts at the occiput (just one example) and are successfully treating endocrine imbalances through working with the fluid tide along the spinal column. Qigong uses other maps still, and achieves physical balance with contact to energy beyond the body through understanding and consciously influencing the field around it. Anthroposophical Medicine and Gnostic teachings map the etheric and astral fields as part of our human biological systems and, again, treat physical imbalance from there, the field beyond the body.

Together, layered one on top of another, the maps from these diverse cultures and systems of medicine weave a complete and multidimensional figure of who we are and how we actually work. The many layers are like an invisible living matrix of the physical anatomy and physiology of our bones, cardiovascular system, muscles, tendons, organs, skin, endocrine system, nervous system, and digestive system—all of which are wrapped together in an intricate and interconnected weaving of form and function.

"Everything is energy, and that's all there is to it. Match the frequency of the reality you want, and you cannot help but get that reality. It can be no other way. This is not philosophy. This is physics." —**Albert Einstein**

Though this information appears sometimes contradictory, or doesn't align across cultures, there are patterns that hold steady. Tracking across systems, I find the main consistency to be in how energy moves and along which currents. The maps and exercises here reflect that—the universal order of the macro movements of energy through and beyond your body. Becoming familiar with these is a solid first step in learning who you are and how to care for yourself. The micro movements, as I will call them, are what alternative practitioners in diverse fields spend their lives studying and practicing in order to treat their patients.

We are currents of energy that move in spirals in these directions:

East-West Pole
energy current

North-South Pole
energy current

Atomic Energy Current at 1/2 points
of cardinal directions

There is no controversy or discrepancy across these multiple systems of science and medicine that we are indeed fields of information that extend from our insides to out far beyond us.

While these fields can be touched and treated by a perceptive practitioner, they can also be cleansed and cleared by you! The meditations and images below show you how, with your mind's eye, to clear stagnation and treat imbalance yourself.

PERCEPTION AND PROTECTION:
A NEW WAY OF SEEING

If we allow ourselves to imagine this possibility, that we exist in layers, and become curious enough about it to start feeling into it, we begin to shift not just our idea of the body and what it is, but also our relationship to the world around us. We begin to feel it in new ways. This is a form of protection, because we can now access information that perhaps we cannot even see, such as potential toxicity, bugs, viruses, or other threats to our health and safety. We perceive them through feelings, images, perhaps a thought, or a word or a dream.

This level of perception has many applications. One of them is noticing if you are getting sick and doing something to stay well before it reaches the body systems and organs.

Your energy field becomes an important part of your immune system. We could also perceive it as your nervous system since it is picking up information it perceives in the field around you (whether through smell, auditory perceptions, or felt perception) and then transfers that information into your physical body. Your body then responds. When it's safe, you can rest in health, with active immunity, digestion, reproductive capacity, and balance in your organs. When it's not safe, biological functions are compromised. This is an energetic view that explains the intimate relationship between your nervous system and your immune system.

In understanding about your energy field, you assume the power for being healthy and safe. It is in your hands, in your heart, in your potential, and in your energetic field. This isn't the psychology of illness. Rather, it is the power to direct your thoughts to clear your energetic field and strengthen your immunity and protection. It is vibrational medicine, and it is very real.

"I know it was real. I felt it." —**Jennifer Hina**

One of the ways that I care for myself is by lying down to rest in the afternoon. Even at the extreme cost of putting my children on a TV show and outsourcing their education to a screen, I will lie down, on the ground, face up, no pillows, and collect myself.

The thing is that, unless I do these exercises described below, I never really rest. This is how I know they are real. I feel them. I feel the layers and layers of stress and activity swirling through my self, my mind, and my physical body dissipate when I direct my mind in these specific ways. The impact they have on both my mental state and physical being is profound, and when I fully surrender to this power, I dip into a deep reservoir, a well of nourishment that I have never found another way.

The chakras, to start, are like the individual mouths of the energy body that map themselves in seven major points along the north-south pole of our physical bodies. The points along the meridian maps in Chinese Medicine can also be called chakras because they, too, are vortexes where energy enters and exits the physical body. This brings the number of chakras to 694 (Francesca McCartney, Academy for Intuitive Medicine lecture September 15, 2020). Each one, as they teach in Yoga and Ayurveda, is associated with a specific color, sound, vibration, flower, or sacred geometric configuration. These vibrational qualities are ways of speaking to the chakra, reaching into it to clear or open it, the way we do our physical bodies with a fast or cleanse. Without even knowing the specific attributes of each energy vortex, you can touch into your own body by directing your mind as described below.

EXERCISES FOR EMBODIMENT AND ENERGETIC PROTECTION

These exercises are based on original body energy maps from Ayurveda and Yogic practices as well as more recent interpretive healing modalities such as Craniosacral therapy, Polarity therapy, Therapeutic Touch, Qigong Healing Touch, and Touch for Health.

The chakra field is one layer of entering and exiting the physical form, and we can attend to it through awareness and meditation.

The solar plexus is another main entrance and exit place mapped from the energetic body onto the physical one, and it mediates between energy, emotions, and our physical health. It is the area beneath your sternum or breast plate and above your belly button.

Then, there are fields that move energy through three dimensions just beyond the body that can be treated through directing awareness and intention through their currents. The currents move through the North-South pole, the East-West pole, and halfway points between the cardinal directions, as we see in the sacred patterns set up in nature that allow strength, integrity, regeneration, and fertility. The patterns at the heart of a sunflower or in the cross section of a nautilus shell, for example, reflect what we have come to call Sacred Geometry. It is the divine order reflected in the proportions of life as it regenerates itself in nature.

GLOWING: LEARNING HOW TO "TURN IT ON"

One's deepest expression of self *is* the protection. It moves out in a field that sets up a boundary that, when intact, will not be penetrated. But life, from the beginning, and often even before we are born, rips at the cords that weave this most protective shield. Assistance in clearing it and then reinforcing it is essential. Experienced practitioners of Intuitive Medicine and other forms of Energy Medicine can often help do this, and then instruct on exercises that will reinforce this protection. Some of them are described below.

Juice it Up - *this practice, also referred to as 'opening and clearing the chakras,' is actually a shortcut to daily restoration and rejuvenation. Simply by bringing your focus to these energetic powerhouses of your body, you boost the function of the organ systems located beneath them, including the endocrine glands. Within 15 minutes you have not only a face lift, but an entire body lift. And, if you find yourself feeling slow, sluggish, or tired when you are done, rest assured that your body is recalibrating and taking the rest it needs to restore itself.*

Lie on the ground, face up, body relaxes into the ground.

First chakra: **Bring** your attention to the base of your body. Just in front of the coccyx, the very bottom of your sacrum. Imagine a spiral there, and let your imagination spin that spiral. Clockwise, counterclockwise, clockwise again.

Second chakra: **Move** your attention up to the lower abdomen. Just above your pubic bone and beneath your belly button. Again, imagine the spiral. Turn it—clockwise, counterclockwise, and clockwise again.

Repeat clockwise, counterclockwise, and clockwise as your move up the chakras

Third chakra: Solar Plexus

Fourth chakra: Heart

Fifth chakra: Throat

Sixth chakra: Third Eye between the eyebrows

Seventh chakra: Top of the head

Close by bringing your attention to the field around you. Imagine an egg of light surrounding you and a glow emanating out from deep inside of you to fill that egg.

Chakra centers

Start to notice… Take notes on any shifts you see in your life—whether relational, psychological, emotional, or physical. When energy is cleared out of the chakras, we are able to meet our lives with more clarity, which impacts how we show up in relationship to ourselves, to others, and to the world around us.

LEARNING TO READ "GUT FEELINGS"

The third chakra corresponds with an area we also call the solar plexus bowl, just above the belly button and beneath the breastplate. It is the headquarters of our personal power, as it is mapped onto the body. Just knowing this may help you discern information that arrives directly there, in your gut. When your gut responds or reacts to something, it is a very direct cue for you to take note. Notice the sensation in your body and PAY ATTENTION. It's communicating something that your brain may not yet understand.

The more you care for the "hygiene" of this spiritual anatomy, the cleaner and clearer the signals and their meanings become.

One of my all-time beloved and esteemed teachers, Damaris Jarboux, founder of the Center Place and the Body Energy Center, and a Founder of The National Qigong Association, holds the highest certifications as a Senior Qigong Teacher and Clinical Practitioner. Her knowledge, experience, and impact as a teacher and practitioner is recognized internationally. We have her to thank for the following exercise.

Stoke the Fire, Fuel the Flames - *the fire of digestion is recognized across medical systems, new and old, for its power to transform food to nutrients that build and sustain the physical body. What is less well-known is the energetic quality fire plays in our biological story. Fire, as an essence, transforms matter to energy, cloudiness to clarity, and venom to medicine. It is critical not only for its power to digest food, but also its ability to digest and assimilate life. The exercise below helps to stoke your fire, not only clearing your organs for efficient and effective digestion, but also for clear expression of power and purpose in the world. When the solar plexus area is cleared and open, your true self shines through.*

Lie down, on your back, face up, soften your face, your eyes, your jaw.

Bring your attention to your solar plexus region, just below your xyphoid process (breast plate) and above your belly button. Picture a circle there, or a bowl, below your rib cage and around the upper region of your belly.

Place your two hands, cupped, above your solar plexus region, with your fingers relaxing down onto your belly in the formation of a line that runs from your belly button to the bottom of your sternum. So the right hand is on the bottom, and your pinky placed softly in your belly button. The left hand is above it, with the left pinky resting gently against the right hand forefinger.

Imagine energy pouring out of your heart, down through your arms and hands, into the solar plexus, melting away any residue there.

Imagine a circle around the edge of the solar plexus region. Place fingers on circumference of bowl, tracing around the edge, as you breathe in a full breath and out a full breath.

Bring fingers back to line in middle of solar plexus. Invite the area to soften and clear again.

Use your right hand to spiral energy clockwise, lifting your hand up and out while you imagine gathering and pulling energy toward the sky. Repeat in a counterclockwise then clockwise direction.

Resting fingers still on that line, imagine a golden egg surrounding you. It's mesh and completely closed. Notice if there are any rips in the mesh, and imagine pulling your energy up and out to seal or repair them. Breathe, inviting yourself to glow and fill that egg.

Relax hands and rest into sensation of your body and being. Bring attention back to room as you transition out of supine position.

Come to a still standing position. Notice your breath. Your face. Your body. If you notice any tension invite it to go down, into the ground.

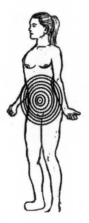

Solar plexus

There is something that happens when you start to open your awareness and reclaim your sensitivity where you begin to feel more acutely not just yourself, but everything around you. Be aware that your solar plexus is literally taking in information from what is around you and trying to digest it.

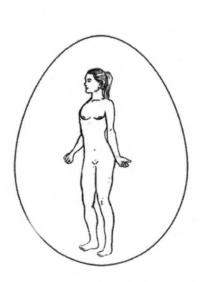

The Golden Egg, An Invisible Shield of Protection

The exercise below is yet another way of clearing your personal space of any energies that may cloud it and opening it for you to fill. Again, this is one form of immunity that we can take charge of to help protect ourselves from the threat of agents that take us down—any of the many invaders that potentially compromise our health. This exercise, together with the two described above, not only addresses the energetic and spiritual bodies, but opens the physical body as well, so that it can radiate energy into the space around you. This creates what I have heard called a golden egg of protection that we touched on in the meditation above. Carry your awareness of it with you at all times, and watch the world re-shape itself around you.

This too comes from esteemed Teacher, Clinical Nurse and Practitioner, Damaris Jarboux.

Own Your Space - *traditionally referred to as the belt channel exercise, this practice helps open and widen the protective shield that radiates through your east-west current. It helps YOU fill your space, so that no one else can. Opening and protecting a greater space around you not only enhances your sensitivity of perception, I find it also helps with digestion, both of food through the stomach and intestines and with lived experiences and your emotional responses to them.*

Lie in supine position (face up), imagine a spiral of energy circling around your waist, like a belt, at the surface of your skin or just beyond.

Imagine moving this spiral counterclockwise, generating energy to turn it left, then right in a clockwise direction.

Notice if it moves with ease or feels stuck.

Notice if the path is circular or oval.

Turn it counterclockwise again.

Imagine moving this spiral up from the waist to the solar plexus area. Again, circle it counterclockwise, clockwise, then counterclockwise again.

Move this spiral up, stopping at each chakra to allow it to turn three to nine times each direction, counterclockwise, clockwise, then counterclockwise again. All the way to the crown chakra (the seventh) then back down to the feet, pausing at the knees and ankles (lesser chakra centers).

Finish by imagining the spiral of energy enveloping your body and turning both directions to generate a field of protection and space around you, like the golden egg pictured here.

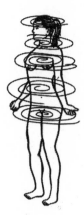

If you practice this daily, you may begin to notice that people respond differently to you. You may notice old patterns in relationships start to shift, and you may feel freedom where once you were bound or confounded. Perhaps you caught a glimpse of respect where before you did not, or cooperation where before you were alone. Take notes and have courage to give voice to what you see and will now insist upon.

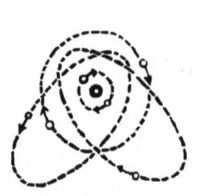

The energetic anatomy of an atom

QIGONG - AN ANCIENT PRACTICE MAKES WAVES

Qigong, while all the rage in the growing movement of Alternative Medicine, is still a foreign and esoteric term that threatens to scare away those just dabbling in healthy lifestyles. How can we reclaim the principles of such a brilliant ancient framework for health and healing and breathe new life into it?

If we start with the understanding or knowledge that Qigong, as a philosophy, is what laid the foundation for both Chinese Medicine (as we know it today) and for Tai Chi (a world-renowned form of movement proven to increase circulations and stamina, improve balance and strength, and quiet the mind while enhancing health), then we might stand a chance of bringing this multifaceted idea and practice to modern times.

Qigong, though recognized as a form of clinical medicine in China for centuries, is another doorway into understanding yourself, your energetic bodies, and how they relate to the natural elements. Qi (Chi - vital force, energy) and gong (the power to produce an effect) has proven itself through mastery of energy once practiced by individuals in ancient Chinese culture. While much of its mystique and magic have been lost to the short attention span and busy requirements of life today, its maps and basic principles remain as whispers of reminders of how we might claim our own power back in the field of medicine, and how we practice wellness in our own lives.

The maps of Qigong clearly and specifically illustrate the five elements as they are found in nature (earth, water, fire, metal, and wood), onto and into and around the body.

This means that Qigong, as a Spiritual Science, traces the essential nature of what earth is, or water is, or fire is, or metal and wood, from its most metaphysical manifestation, down into its physical reality. It acknowledges that before something is matter, it is energy. There is a clear line, a continuum, a thread, that translates this energy down through space into matter.

There are points of intersection along this thread where we can label certain attributes of what later we might call "wood" or "metal." For example, Kindness will first be experienced as something we call Virtue or Spirit. Then, it steps down into a more concrete experience of the mind, or in the mental field, called decision-making. When the path of decision-making is not free and clear, we may have an even more embodied experience of Anger or Power. Anger and power are emotions, but they live in the physical form of the liver and the gall bladder. Anger and power are the human embodiment of the element we know as wood. And so, first Qigong and later Chinese Medicine tracks a Spiritual experience down through the mind, into the emotional body, throughout the physical body.

While this may not make sense at the moment, there are basic maps you can learn and practice as part of an Earth Medicine Practice that honor these relationships and support health in your body and throughout the many layers of your life. One layer of the beautiful, poetic, and very real map of the energy body as laid out in Qigong is described for you below, including simple practices to use at home.

A GLIMPSE OF THE THREE TREASURES, THE ENERGETIC WAREHOUSES OF YOUR BODY

In Medical Qigong, we look at the energy of the body as being stored in three separate "warehouses." Jing, in the lower abdomen, Chi in the middle abdomen, and Shen in the head and above. Let's take a look at each one.

"Health in the Body, Peace in the Spirit, Love in the Heart." —Prayer, **Alexandra Durlene**

JING - THE DEEP BODY

Jing is the deepest source of energy in the physical body. It is the deep well. One's pure essence. It is believed to be stored in the lower abdomen. In women, this is the womb space, both real and symbolic. In men as well, it is below the naval and sits above the perineum, or pelvic floor. In both men and women, Jing plays a significant role in regulating the sex organs and hormones and in supporting an individual's fertility. In a western scientific model of the body and human health, we might compare Jing to adrenal energy that is stored in the glands just above the kidneys.

Initially, Jing is one's genetically inherited storehouse of energy. We are born with a supply of Jing, and it reflects our parents' health, particularly the mother, at conception and birth. Jing energy is impacted over time through lifestyle choices and diet. Anything that taxes the adrenal glands or "burns the candle at both ends," if prolonged, can reduce Jing energy. Fortunately Jing can be restored by food and energy practices such as Qigong. It is believed to come from the Earth/nature, and practices that gather and balance the Earth's energy can restitute Jing. Walking in nature, directed-specific Qigong practices, choosing specific foods and eating them in good proportion, and right rhythms can all help increase ones Jing.

Ultimately, increasing Jing alleviates the feeling of being deeply tired. Exhausted. Depleted. It's like filling the well back up with clean, fresh water again. Restoring Jing may also help restore balance in the endocrine system to help with menstrual irregularities, trouble sleeping, depression, blood-sugar imbalance, and kidney challenges.

Fill the Well - a meditation for building Jing - *this exercise is deceivingly simple. Please, allow yourself to let all tension go down into the ground before you even begin. Then, soften your brow and let go of your mind. From there, allow yourself to listen and to receive silence. With time and practice, you'll create deep, at first invisible, change.*

Stand feet hip width apart, knees slightly bent, tail bone dropped. Shoulders relaxed. Jaw relaxed. Eyes soft.

Bring hands in a soft, open position in front of your pubic bone to form globe with hands, thumbs connected, four fingers of each hand touching.

Move your hands in the shape of a rectangle, from lower left hip across pubic bone to lower right hip. Up to bottom of right rib cage, across navel to left rib cage and down to left hip again. Repeat at least 3x in each direction.

FEEDING THE WELL - HOW TO NOURISH JING

It should come as no surprise that whole, unadulterated foods will nourish Jing. Fruits and vegetables in their pure, unprocessed, un-juiced forms. Whole grains, dairy products, meats, fowl, fish. Dark foods, in particular, are thought to increase Jing in the body. Below is a list of foods thought to specifically nourish Jing. These are the foods that draw deep earth essence up out of the ground, through the seed, merging it with light from above, and thus, offering you the same gift.

- Rest, deep sleep.

- Animal meats including liver, beef, chicken, pork

- Beans including black, kidney, lentils, aduke

- Congee including barley, oats, rice, sweet rice

- Seaweeds

- Dark leafy greens including dandelion, kelp, spinach, watercress

 Fruits including avocados, figs, grapes, dates

Bone broths, including chicken, beef, pork, wild game

Molasses

CHI - AN ENERGY OF EXCHANGE

Chi is the energy in exchange in our daily actions and interactions. It is the energy we use to plant a garden. Chi is one's pure *energy*, versus the pure *essence* we refer to when we talk about Jing. Chi is located or stored in the middle abdomen, which extends from the heart through solar plexus, the area just above the navel.

Chi is also the current of energy that runs through the meridians, the lines along the body that carry the energetic constitution of the gross body organs such as the liver, gall bladder, stomach, spleen, heart, or small intestines. Meridians are like rivers and creeks that carry water, in this case energy, throughout the "earth" of our bodies. When they get "dammed," and energy cannot flow freely, your health suffers, both on a physical level and an energetic level (which can be emotional or spiritual). Acupuncture is one way we have of breaking up a dam in the river and setting this energy free again. Whether one is suffering back pain or just feels "off," needles into specific points along the body can help restore one's sense of well-being.

One's Chi, or everyday energy, is sourced and strengthened most through the heart and the gut. So, it is directly related to one's love and engagement with true passion and interests. One's true appetite, and the pursuit of what truly feeds you, is essential to maintaining the health of your Chi. Other tools for supporting Chi include practices like Yoga that opens the heart, meditation, physical activity (especially the ones that delight you), and devotional practices.

Like Jing, Chi plays a critical role in regulating the immune/endocrine/neurological systems.

Calm the Fire, Steady the Storm - a meditation for balancing Chi - *this exercise is like lacing Zen through the space around you. Creating calm in the kitchen, I could have called it, as I will do it early in the morning before the sun has even risen or my boys have shown their wildly alive faces. It evens out the currents of energy inside of me, and this translates into the space around me. Remi says it the best when he, who truly knows my reactive and abrupt side, describes me as "All calm and centered. You know, how you do your meditation and magic hands." I thank Donna Eden* *for bringing this through and translating it across time and cultures into our modern forms of Energy Medicine.*

Stand with feet hip width apart. Let tailbone drop to the ground. Relax shoulders and jaw. Soften the eyes.

Let hands fall to either side of thighs, palms facing out. Inhale in through the top of the head and out through the bottoms of the feet at least three times.

Bring hands to prayer position in front of heart and breathe again, being sure to let body drop and relax into the ground.

Raise the right hand to the sky, facing palm up, and push left hand to the ground, facing palm down. Stretch energy with intention out from the heart, into and beyond the hands. Relax, breathe, then release hands back to prayer position at the heart.

Alternate side, again pushing one hand palm out toward the sky, one hand palm out toward the ground. Stretch energy out from the heart, through the arms, and beyond the hands. Return to prayer position.

Alternate as many times as feels comfortable and restorative, bringing hands to prayer position between each exercise.

Finish in prayer position. Relax hands down to side. Breathe through the top of the head down out the bottom of the feet and give thanks.

FOODS THAT STEADY THE STORM - HOW TO BALANCE CHI

Alive foods will feed the aliveness in your body, supporting the oxygenation of your blood cells and the sense of strength and vigor you feel. So green foods, wild foods, organic, fresh, unpackaged foods are all in service to support the health of your Chi.

 Love, even the memory or visualization of it

 Fresh fruits including grapefruit, oranges, plums, raspberries, strawberries, kiwi, black current, blackberries

 Meats including duck, rabbit, and beef

- Wild greens including watercress, miners lettuce, lambsquarters, purslane, dandelion, yellow dock, parsley, cilantro

- Sprouted seeds including. alfalfa, sunflower, clover

- Unprocessed cereals such as flax, oats, millet, barely, buckwheat, rye

- Easy to digest and assimilate soups and stews

SHEN - MENTAL POWER

Shen is Energy of the Spirit. It is closely associated with heart, but directly influenced by consciousness, the mind, our thoughts, and our visual images. Shen is stored in the third eye, just between one's eyebrows. Initially, one's storehouse of Shen comes from one's supply or excess of Chi. They are partners in financing one's energy, both in the body and the field beyond the body.

As we grow and age, we can nourish and restock Shen in the body through meditative practices or experiences that expand consciousness and awareness. Ultimately these experiences, whether long processes in relationship or work, or facilitated more quickly through Shamanic healings and plant medicine, must be integrated into one's conscious mind and one's body. This includes docking it into the central nervous system and regulating it in relationship to the spinal column and spinal fluid. So, working with Shen is more subtle and harder to see and to document.

Any work one does with Spirit—prayer, forgiveness, or transformation—relates to Shen energy and impacts health on an "energy field" level. The healthier the energy field, the stronger one's immune system is, the safer one's nervous system is, and the more fluid, healthy, and full the endocrine system is.

What holds you up when you can no longer hold yourself? If you have had the bittersweet privilege of falling to your knees in the impossible beauty and complexity of loving life, and losing what you love, then you have already begun the exercise. It helps to first taste the saltiness of loss. And longing. This is where we meet Grace. Yes, it is often hard to see. Harder still to recognize when something lifts us up off the floor to help us keep going, when we think we no longer can. This is when it is helpful to name "God." Call it She, or Her, call it Divinity or Grace. Call it Source or Magic. Call it Yaweh or Allah. Call it Goddess or Gods, Holy Spirit or

Jesus, Salvation, Christ. Hell, I don't care what you call it. Just give it a name. "It" will do for now. Then, feel it please.

 **Give it Up to "God" - a meditation for enhancing Shen** - *the exercise below will assist you in that. It helps you to drop the tension of "needing to know" from the body, and while it is essentially a grounding exercise, it also helps to free your mind. In any spiritual endeavor, the essential first step is to get grounded, firmly rooted in your body, on the Earth.*

Practice this exercise first (even before those listed above) as a way to drop down into the felt sense of your body. Here, you encounter what is true, built into you brick by brick in a cellular level. "The body does not lie" we say in Somatic therapy. Notice where you are holding or feel blocked, and breathe into that place. This way you bypass the brain and take the shortcut to feeling well.

Stand with legs shoulder width apart, slightest bend at the knees. Let your tailbone drop. Relax your feet into the ground and imagine a camera lens in the middle of the sole of each foot, opening to a wide aperture. Relax your face.

Bring your attention to each body part, as named, and imagine dropping tension in the body from here on down into the ground as you inhale in and exhale it all out with each part.

Say to your ankles: "let go down into the ground"

Say to your knees: "let go down into the ground"

Say to your hips: "let go down into the ground"

Say to your top of the head at crown point down through the sacrum, tailbone: "let go down into the ground"

Say to your right shoulder: "let go down into the ground"

Say to your right elbow: "let go down into the ground"

Say to your right wrist: "let go down into the ground"

Pause and notice if you feel different in right arm than left arm

Say to your left shoulder: "let go down into the ground"

Say to your left elbow: "let go down into the ground"

Say to your left wrist: "let go down into the ground"

Pause again. And notice sensation in right and left arms

Say to your face and jaw: "let go down into the ground"

Soften your eyes

Breathe three times in through the top of your head, imagining breath cleansing through the body and down out the feet

---

THE FOOD OF SURRENDER - HOW TO FEED SHEN

Foods that detoxify your system, from whatever is blocking pure consciousness, will support your Shen energy. These practices are cleansing and clarifying:

- Clear, healthy thoughts

- Clean Air

- Inspiring poetry, words

- Fermented foods kimchee, sauerkraut, pickled onions, etc.

- Miso

- Apple parsley Dressing with Cayenne

- Cilantro

- Celery

- Green apples

- Medicinal teas that cleanse, clear, and balance including chrysanthemum, dandelion, burdock, lemon, balm, elderflower, chamomile

A New Language for Love

What do you do first thing in the morning, when you wake up? This is a pivotal, threshold moment where your attention is deep and connected. Connected to you, connected to source, connected to past: present: future possibilities for who you are and how you will show up in the world. If you take this time to touch into that, to be quiet and listen to the dreams or sensations that are ushering you into the day, or to listen to the energy that is showing up for the day ahead, you will harness new energy and awareness. It is delicious and not to be missed! It is possibly the doorway into your own language, your first step to true fulfillment, and yes, I can't help but call it love.

Below are basic morning wake-up practices that harness the circular nature of how energy moves. The first one opens your joints and starts to ignite the movement of energy through your meridian system. It is gentle enough for a wake-up exercise and stimulating enough to get you in your body and quickly prepared for breakfast, or driving, or whatever your morning requires. The second one stimulates blood flow and circulation of oxygen throughout the body. It also tones muscle.

 **Open the Joints, Circles** - *stand with feet hip width apart or aligned with shoulders. Let your tailbone be heavy, as if it is dropping down into the ground. Relax your face, your jaw, your eyes, your shoulders.*

Circle the joints of the body, three times in each direction, clockwise and counterclockwise. In this order:

    neck

    left shoulder

    left elbow

    left wrist

    right shoulder

    right elbow

    right wrist

    hips

knees

ankles

Awaken the Meridians - *this exercise awakens energy along meridian lines, helping to disperse stagnant Chi and wake up.*

Stand with legs hip width apart, feet facing forward, tailbone dropped.

Relax jaw, relax eyes, relax face, and top of the head.

Cup hands into gentle fist (not clinging too hard).

Use fists to gently tap from the bottom to top of each limb

right leg

left leg

right arm (from wrist to shoulders)

left arm (from wrist to shoulders)

torso, from hips to shoulders, front

and back

Finish by tapping on your breast plate.

Feel your body and relax your tailbone and let your energy drop again down into the ground.

READING THE SIGNS

The Metaphysics of medicine are just that - Metaphysics. They reach beyond what we can see, hear, taste, or smell and propose that there is an energetic field that exists beyond matter and informs how matter shapes itself and behaves. They do not deny laws of science or principles of physics, but rather flesh them out and beg to balance them with principles of intuition, what we have called the Feminine Model for health. There are new discoveries made daily in the field of science that both expand our awareness of how things actually work and shift old models that we once thought were true.

Here at the threshold of a new era in medicine, it is time to acknowledge the many forms of Alternative treatments, therapies, and medical systems that have existed across the globe, some of them for centuries, and also stood up to the rigors of scientific inquiry and statistical studies. All of them, when applied correctly, allow for fluidity in our concept of body and health, and have proven themselves capable of entirely transforming both individual and communal health. The key to their success is a richer understanding of how they work, who we are, how we work, and how we employ these practitioners and the practices in the way that allows them to be effective on our journeys to true, vibrant health, or *embodiment*.

The breezes at dawn have secrets to tell you.

Don't go back to sleep.

You must ask for what you really want.

Don't go back to sleep.

People are going back and forth across the doorsill

where the two worlds touch.

The door is round and open.

Don't go back to sleep.

~From Essential Rumi

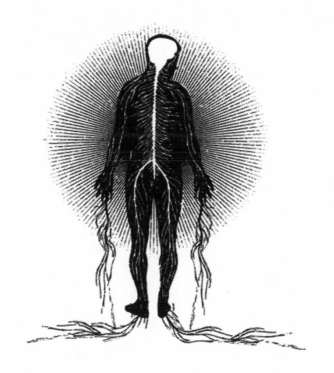

CHAPTER NINE

PSYCHONEUROIMMUNOLOGY:

WHERE MIND AND MEDICINE MEET

on a spiral staircase between past and future

We have already made the connection between the nervous system and the immune system. To add the "psycho" piece, or mental piece to it, we look at beliefs and perceptions of what is true or what is not true.

CONSTRUCTING THE MIND

Each of us houses a different construct of reality. It comes, brick by brick, through our process of conception, birth, early childhood, childhood, adolescence, adulthood, arriving in the place of the elder. The energy in the relationship between father and mother at conception will influence the baby's formation and character, as will its life in-utero and through the process of birth. The child's relationship to mother in the early years, her health and their connection, starts to shape its beliefs about how the world is. The home, its energetic milieu, what the parents say and what they think further shape how the child will think, until it leaves the home and becomes part of the larger culture. Then, the cultural concepts for what is good and bad start to transfer into the individual's perception of good, bad, or normal.

This is not an exposition on good or bad, right, or wrong, but an exploration of how we come to think of things such as: love is not safe, or they won't like me if I'm fat, or I must have money to be well, or I will be successful if I get this job. The subtle and sometimes not subtle signals that society offers us play a significant role in how our brains shape themselves. The formation of the nervous system is therefore tied into the deep-seated beliefs we construct throughout our lives. Our perception of love and safety springs from that.

Traumatic experiences further shape and impact the development in the body. Significant trauma is even passed down through generations, because when we experience a truly traumatic event or episode, the energy of fear steps down from the field into the body and closes the building blocks of our physical systems. This closure is a form of protection that allows for survival. Like closing and locking a door when someone is coming at you in a scary way. Often though, the door remains closed, and this, while only an energetic closure at first, becomes physical. We see it as lesions in Craniosacral therapy. There are literal places in the body that are sealed, like scar tissue on the skin, and this inhibits the flow, not just of energetic information, as carried along the nervous system, but of blood flow, oxygen, enzymes, and nutrients required for full bodily health.

The field of Psychoneuroimmunology, mentioned throughout the book, has recognized these relationships, between the mind and its belief patterns, the nervous system and the immune system. How they relate and interact is at the heart of this new field of medicine and a foundational piece in restoring balance to the body. The endocrine system, still very much a mystery to Western Medicine in how it produces and maintains balance of the hormones essential to health, is greatly impacted by the relationship between how we think, feel, and protect or defend ourselves. Taking a bigger view of the body, where it starts and where it ends, helps us to understand more clearly the relationships at hand here and how to support them.

One of the deepest meditations I have found for accessing and influencing my own endocrine system is by bringing my attention to the space behind my eyes, down from the center of my head, between my ears. There is a well here, an empty space we call the third ventricle where cerebrospinal fluid emerges and joins the river of fluid that runs from the brain down along the spine to the sacrum, then back up again. It is adjacent to the pineal gland, the Holy Grail of the endocrine system that helps to regulate our sleep patterns, and is believed to influence the balance of the rest of our hormones. The pineal gland is also associated with the third eye and intuitive vision. Finding our way into it, through our mind's eye, is like finding a palace, a Holy space, a well that we can rest into and where we can restore ourselves.

An Endocrine-balancing Exercise: the cistern in back of your eyes - *connecting with the sacred space in the Third Ventricle and pineal gland. This powerful meditation came to me via Dee Mertz, a practitioner of Intuition Medicine as it is taught at Dr. Francesca McCartney's Academy of Intuition. While Dr. McCartney refers to this location as the Meditation Palace, and offers the groundbreaking idea that "meditation is a location," I have found it to match the concepts I learned in the school of biodynamic Craniosacral therapy and what we know as the Third Ventricle. It is described in depth below.*

Sit quietly, legs crossed, or feet uncrossed and contacting the floor, relax your shoulders, your eyes, your jaw, your face, the top of your head.

Bring your attention to your breath. Allow it to fill and empty your body in a slow, comfortable rhythm.

Bring your awareness to your head. Imagine a cord dropping down through the top of your head, down out the base of your body. Allow it to intersect a cord that you imagine passes laterally from ear to ear, and one that comes in between your eyebrows, from the front to the back of your head, exiting at the top of the occipital bone. There is a center place where these three lines intersect. Allow your attention to pause there.

Imagine this is an empty place. A room. A space. An opening. A place for you to rest. What does it look like? What does it feel like? Are there colors or smells that emerge there for you? Allow your imagination to suggest a place of retreat and restitution.

Notice the sensations in your body as you connect with this place. Allow your breath to fill and empty. Allow your weight to drop and the fluid potential of your water body to fill your cells, giving you just the right medicine for now. Cleansing, restoring, reshaping, remembering balance into your physical self.

THE FUTURE OF MEDICINE

Running this morning, I am struck by the perseverance and insistence of what we call weeds. Also known as medicinal plants, they are the inspiration of pharmaceutical medicines, before pharmacies even existed.

I have been told that, at the turn of the century in the 1900s, Homeopathy and Allopathic Medicine were competing head-to-head for the main presence in hospitals: the dominant form of medicine we would all come to use and rely on over the next century.

Homeopathy harvests the medicinal properties of our weeds. The plants that western science now deems toxic and potentially dangerous, the ones that don't give up. EVER. The ones that recover from wildfire, frost, toxic chemical overload, adjustments in our climate, and magnetic fields. The ones that survive despite the human and environmental changes that fluctuate around them. The ones that have the power to kill. That also have the power to give life. They can be used as salves, sprays, tinctures, in capsule form. And one plant has so many applications, from bringing on menses and restoring health to the reproductive system to calming the nervous system or eliminating parasites and bacteria. But this form of medicine lost the battle for a profitable future in hospitals and medical care and was shelved, for the most part.

As the crisis of clean water, clean air, sources for clean energy, and waste disposal become increasingly a mainstream issue, it becomes easier to argue the point that connecting the health of the earth with the health of our bodies is in the best interest of all of us. And that possibly this was the initial design: humans and plants in intimate relationship and interdependence. What is one's waste is the other's life force. What is one's strength is the other's weakness. To protect and assist one, we must protect and assist the other.

If we start to shift our perception to a wide field that entertains the possibility that we exist beyond our bodies, if only simply as a nervous system, and the protection and well-being of the nervous system is essential to the health and well-being of one's body and soul, then we start to see and take interest in things that interrupt our nervous systems. Things like stress, toxic chemicals, artificial forms of stimulants, emotional assault, pharmaceuticals that overload the liver, toxic waste from factory pollution, all of the things we have deemed ok, necessary, even beneficial to meet the needs of a growing population. And then we may begin to see differently. And care of ourselves will naturally extend beyond ourselves, and change, for the better, everything we touch.

Creating change starts with making your own Power Shield Medicine. The two recipes below are broad spectrum options to fight colds and flus, to stoke fires of digestion, and support health for the entire family, at very low cost.

 Save Our Lungs Elderberry Syrup - *for winter wellness I marvel, again and again, at the elderberry's ability to keep us well when winter colds and flus are coming and everyone else is sick. You can even make your own at home.*

Approx. 1 cup of dried elderberries
1 to 2 oz fresh ginger (optional to add heat and expand healing capacity)
Confidence
6 cups water

In a heavy saucepan, bring elderberries and water to a boil, reduce heat, and let simmer approx. 40 minutes. Turn off flame, and let sit until cool. Strain liquid through a fine strainer or a cloth bag (like one used to make nut or oat milk), perhaps mashing elderberries at bottom with the back of a wood spoon to get last bits of juice.

Add this elderberry liquid to the following:
1/2 to 1 cup liquor to preserve (Scotch and Vodka are good options)
1/4 to 1/2 cup honey to sweeten
Reverence

Return all combined ingredients to heavy saucepan. Let boil over low flame for approx. 30 minutes, so alcohol evaporates. Add honey and/or sugar. Let cool and pour into preferred bottles.

 Back to Your Roots Ginger Syrup - *ginger is a medical root through and through. Known for its heat and high mineral content, it can be applied as a cold remedy or ingested for stomach ailments. In Ayurveda, we say it stokes Agni, or increases digestive*

fire. I make a simple syrup and give it to my children when they feel ill with a cold, or put it in soda water with lime before dinner when I want to feed my appetite, or if I have a headache.

1 chunk of ginger - about the size of 2 fingers
3 to 4 cups water
Self-Assurance
1/3 cup honey

Cut ginger into slices and peel, casually. Not necessary to remove all of the peel. Place in saucepan with water on stove at medium heat, and bring to a boil. Reduce heat, and let simmer approx. 20 minutes. Turn off heat. Add honey, and stir until dissolved. Let cool. Place in glass jar, labeled, in fridge. Use as desired. Ours seems to last three weeks or so.

It's winter here again in San Francisco, and the rain is coming down. The boys and I drove over the bridge and into the city for a rare pilgrimage to eat Dim Sum. Restaurants are closed because of the Covid-19 pandemic, but I know where to get roast duck, and they discovered a window with pork buns and dumplings. So we all found a way to our hearts' delights, and as impossible as standing in line seemed to young American boys, we stood in line to wait for food.

"We stand in line to learn patience," I had to tell them. This is something else I learned living in Latin America as a young adult—the beauty and importance of standing in line. So much can happen when we are forced to stand in place. I call them the magical weavings that appear in shared space, in the time between time, side by side with people you don't know, but are there now with you, on a shared path.

For me, in the end, the pause felt too brief to settle their high-tech nervous systems, but at least we had the lived experience together.

Today, a day later, I am dipping my left-over duck into the 5-spice sauce, then folding it into a rice flour bun with some fresh pea shoots and sliced jalapeño from my own kitchen, and I am feeling into the deep satisfaction of taking responsibility for my own nourishment. Is this an arrival point? Is this the making of a true adult, the assuming responsibility for feeding myself, in the very way I need to be fed today? Yes, we are back in winter. The Northern shield. The place of taking responsibility. The symbolic season of adulthood. Since I have come to visit it so many times, I feel more ease and possibility than I used to. And even a glimmer of desire and delight, knowing now that the only way through it is through it. Might as well send love into the contractions and surrender into the birth of an eventual elder.

So, I am savoring my roasted duck bun with pea shoots and jalapeño as I offer this up again: food cannot ever really be separated from love. It's in our biology. The impulse and instinct to eat is wired as deep as the human heart. It's laced and threaded in spirals that wrap into the intricate play of love, bone, blood, fascia, tissue, muscles, and the brilliant organ systems we eventually become.

This weaving, winding, wrapping, spiraling dance does not stop at the surface of our skin though. It pulses and expands out from us and beyond us, transmitted through our hearts and minds, our souls, our spirits, and ultimately our deepest desires. The question is, how do we discover them? How do we find the way? When there are so many conflicting signals and road signs that don't add up, it's easier than ever to miss the lights trying to lead you along. It's more important than ever that our adults and elders keep the torches lit to show their youth the way.

My job, as I have come to see it in the stark, sometimes cold and constantly unapologetic mirror of the Northern shield is to weave the metaphor back into the medicine. When we awaken to the body held in our words and our images, when we reclaim the power of poetry and breathe life into it, the way Shamans have across cultures, continents, and time frames since as long as we can track the relationship of humanity to medicine. It is then we begin to see who we really are, and how medicine really works.

Here in the winter of a global pandemic, our institutions are as stressed and exhausted as the individuals who inhabit them. Our social realities are collapsing, as we have resorted to social isolation and distancing as a remedy to alleviate the onslaught of Covid-19 patients taxing our medical organizations beyond their capacity to serve. Businesses are scrambling to re-invent themselves and respond to consumers' expectations and demands, as we collectively cling to the comforts that we have previously known.

Beyond the collapse of our social and economic realities, and the disintegration of our schools, businesses, medical institutions, and expectations, there is the ongoing global crisis of mass extinction of entire species of plants and animals. There is also the disappearance of coastal communities and homelands we have depended on not just as reprieve from the relentless expectations of our modern lives, but also for their unsung contributions to the delicate balance of life on planet Earth.

Within the context of such mammoth proportions, some are suggesting that it is women, mothers, who will lose the most here. Our entire orientation in the outside world is shifting as we are kept home to care for our children. It falls on us to find the courage and compassion essential for keeping the fires of our hearths alive and on us to plant the seeds of hope and vision necessary for our children who see life as they have known it coming apart. It is we who feel, down into our bones, the collective panic that comes with such unknowns.

As mothers and fathers, as grandparents and great-grandparents, we are in the unique position to bring new practices and new ideas into our homes. Together with our children, we can resuscitate ancient wisdom for how to live in harmony with who we are and what we really need to survive. The rest is a distraction and will not lead to true fulfillment, wellness, or radiant, unshakeable health.

Winter is cold and internal. And no matter what we do, or don't do, each and every one of us will meet it. But if we meet it in the knowing that we have labored for what is true, for what is good, for what is relevant, and for what truly nourishes each of us, then we can surrender more easily into the heartbreak and loss that winter brings. This is the way to keep a flicker of fire alive, for ourselves and for our children, until summer arrives again.

Some days winter comes too quickly. It is an unanticipated halt in my road to possibility, the one that is escorting me toward profound fulfillment, even joy and delight. The one where I believe I am allowed to have my bliss, even now as an adult with four young children, despite all of the roadblocks and obstacles.

The other day the cold was fast and heavy enough that I almost didn't notice the light that rode in just behind it. It, the light, the warmth, the hope, spring or summer, came through a Latina Mama who was there beside me, helping me clean my home. She, seeing my distraction and upset, and knowing my story, looked at me.

"Solo te queda amar a tus hijos. Amales. Y pensar en ti misma," she said. "Que necsistas tu para tu vida? Solo esto debe de importarlte. Lo que necisitas tu para seguir adelante con tus hijos."

The only thing left to you is to love your children. Love them. And think of yourself. What do you need for YOUR life? Only this should matter to you. What you need to keep moving forward with them.

"Se lo digo a usted como lo digo a mis hijos y a mis papas. Hay que cuidar el corazón."

I say it to you like I say it to my children and to my own parents. You must care for the heart.

I know, because I can see it in her eyes, and because I know her story, that her words come from an Ocean teeming with life and death, with dreams and losses. And that when she says, "Care for yourself," it is not selfishness, but a deep self-love she wants me to claim. She knows the selfless surrender of motherhood, parenthood, is already intact. And she knows that if I don't claim fully and stand fiercely for what it is that nourishes and holds me, if I don't insist upon having this and allow myself to have what I really want, I will not have or be able to give what I am truly here to give my children.

Still, it took the mirror of another mama to show me the magic: "Your Latina Mama archetype showed up for you!"

She was there in my house helping me to detoxify and purify the space that holds my family, my body and, because I know metaphor, I know too that the home is a symbol of the space that holds my mind, my thoughts, and my beliefs. She was there to clear out any old cobwebs of doubt that might block my way to claiming my best version of self and the life I have left to live.

This is how medicine works. Real medicine at least. It comes in layers, cycles, and circles. It happens in relationship and in love. It is there in the mirror of our own reflections that echo back to us over the journey of our storied lives. The trick is, you must find the courage to step into the story. To move out of the comfort zone and into new, unexplored places, both inside yourself, within your relationships, throughout your communities, and beyond. And then, you must be willing to see, to see what is offered back up to you in the impossible, sometimes unimaginable beauty of the metaphors speaking to you through the wild, undomesticated, and unanticipated world.

Then, perhaps even more challenging than seeing life and yourself with your eyes wide open, you must be willing to be seen. Having others witness us in our vulnerability and imperfections is sometimes the hardest of all. But without witnesses, and others to reflect back who we are and how we behave, we don't truly grow. This is part of the divine design of the universe and what it means to be birthed and parented, each and every one of us. It's how we come to know we are truly loved.

Medicine, like nature, is gendered, and must be treated that way. We must make room for the round and spiraling, indirect and receptive attributes of the feminine qualities of life. They are as essential as the linear and direct, targeted, and specific attributes of the male energies that have come to dominate the medical field. If we can start by recognizing the role and place of each, then we can merge two already vibrant paths to health in ways it has never been merged before.

Just like the male and female, there may never be complete understanding. The languages we speak are too different sometimes. That's just the way it is. But with respect and the construction of good bridges between the two, there is the possibility for encountering new frontiers in medicine. I imagine it's like the bonds on the spiraling staircase of DNA that carries the codes of two separate strands of genetic information up into the open space of potential, where it creates what each of us comes to be, in each and every cell, living organ, and organ system in our bodies. Every letter, as we have come to identify each piece of the DNA, needs a bridge across to the other side in order to be viable. This is how new life is made. This is how healthy families and communities unfold. And this is how new and effective systems of medicine must be architected. There are times for directed, linear action and precise, calculated motion. And there is room for large, unplanned circular gestures, ones that are passive and receptive. It requires the balance of male and female, masculine and feminine, directed and receptive, light and dark.

EASILY FIND YOUR FAVORITE RECIPES

Winter Pantry/Staples

Fresh Lemons

Garlic

Onion

Dried cinnamon

Masa flour

Dried Beans

Gluten-free flour

Olive oil

Applesauce

Masa Flour

Chamomile tea

Frozen Bones

Honey

Magnesium Supplement

Winter Recipes

Bitter Tea (p 30)

Sopa del Jardin: Garden Soup (Gazpacho) (p 35)

Fill My Belly Vanilla Cinnamon Cacao (Atole) (p 37)

Vegetarian Papoose (Tamales) (p 42)

Nourish My Kidneys Black Beans (p 43)

Warm My Womb Applesauce Cinnamon Breakfast Bread (p 47)

Soothe my Sorrows Tea (p 49)

Nourish My Bones Broth (p 52)

Sopa Vuelve a la vida: Come back to Life Winter Green Soup (p 54)

Spring Pantry/Staples	Spring Recipes
Garlic	Purification Sauce (p 64)
Parsley, arugula, plus dark greens	Heal Me Chicken Soup (p 66)
Dates	Warm My Belly Bowl (p 69)
Dried grains: rice, millet, barley, buckwheat	Pasta Please Mom Angel Hair with Greens (p 71)
Lemon	
Onion	Rainbow Flower Salad (p 75)
Ginger	Make Me Hum Jasmine Tea (p 80)
Dried pasta	Balance My Life Dandelion & Bibb Salad (p 84)
Jasmine tea	
Celery	It's Running Smoothly Now Celery and Dates (p 87)
Chlorella	

Summer Pantry/Staples	**Summer Recipes**
Dried root and flowers	Medicine from leaves and flowers (p 99)
Nut Milks of choice	Wild Greens Salad (p 100)
Masa Flour	Give Me Cream Non-dairy Dessert (p 102)
Olives	Homemade Handmade Tortillas (p 107)
Olive Oil	Greek Salad (p 108)
Buckwheat	Earthy Buckwheat Waffles (p 110)
Baking soda and powder	Cinnamon Plum Breakfast Desert (p 116)
Hydrogen peroxide	Basil Bath (p 118)
Cinnamon	mouthwash/cleaner/toothpowder (p 121)
Cayenne pepper	Protect Me Green Apple Parsley Dressing (p 122)
Multi-Mineral Supplement	

ll Pantry/Staples

ogurt

Dried Rasperry Leaf

Quinoa

Sesame Seeds

Red Onions

Garlic

Dates

Pumpkin seeds

Ashwagandha

Mezcal

Fall Recipes

Make Me Happy Cherries (Breakfast bowl) (p 131)

Raspberry Leaf Tea (p 133)

Prepare Me Pickled Pink Onions (p 135)

Basic Quinoa (p 136)

Get it together Sesame Dressing (p 139)

Soaked and Roasted Nuts (p 141)

All of My Longings went away Dates and Milk (p 147)

Soften My Vision Mezcal (p 153)

Pepita Salsa (p 157)

Awe-Inspiring Arugula (p 159)

The Energetics of Western Herbs, Peter Holmes

Eating in the Light of the Moon, Anita Johnston

Flower Essence Therapy, Patricia Kaminski and Richard Katz

Foods of the Americas: Native Recipes and Traditions, Fernando and Marlene Divina

When Food is Love, Geneen Roth

Traveling Mercies, Anne Lamott

Like Water for Chocolate, Laura Esquivel

Disobedience of the Daughter of the Sun, Martin Prechtel

Long Life Honey in the Heart, Martin Prechtel

Stealing Benefacio's Roses, Martin Prechtel

Secrets of a Talking Jaguar, Martin Prechtel

Women's Bodies, Women's Wisdom, Christiane Northrop

Woman as Healer, Jeanne Achterberg

The Heart of Listening, Hugh Milne

The Splendid Grain, Rebecca Wood

The Savory Way, Deborah Madison

Life Changing Foods, Anthony William

Healing with Whole Foods, Paul Pitchford

I Ching, Dhiresha McCarver

The Artist's Way, Julia Cameron

The Book of Mastery, Paul Selig

Word, I am the Word, Paul Selig

Tar Baby, Tony Morrison

Wuthering Heights, Emily Bronte

Medical Medium, Anthony William

Foods that Heal, Anthony William

BIBLIOGRAPHY

Achterberg, Jeanne. Adaptation of a talk presented as a closing plenary session, Creating Integ Health Care, Annual Symposium, San Diego, Calif., 1998. Handout to students attending Sayl University, San Francisco, Calif., 2006.

Achterberg, Jeanne. Imagery in Healing. Shamanism and Modern Medicine. Boston: Shambhala Bo 2013.

Barks, Coleman and Moyne, John. The Essential Rumi. Edison: Castle Books, 1997.

Blue, Darcey. shamanaflora.com

Cassarino, Stacie. "Summer Solstice" from Zero at the Bone. © 2009 by Stacie Cassarino. Reprinted by permission of New Issues Press.

Divina, Fernando and Marlene and the Smithsonian National Museum of the Americas. Foods of the Americas: Native Recipes and Traditions. Berkeley: Ten Speed Press, 2004.

Eden, Donna. Energy Medicine: Balancing Your Body's Energies for Optimal Health, Joy and Vitality. New York: The Penguin Group, 2008.

Emoto, Masaru. The Hidden Messages of Water. Atria Books, 2005

Esquivel, Laura. Like Water for Chocolate: A Novel in Monthly Installments with Recipes, Romances and Home Remedies. Anchor Books, Random House, 1989.

Feinstein, David and Krippner, Stanley. The Mythic Path: Discovering the Guiding Stories of Your Past—Creating a Vision for Your Future. 3rd Edition. Santa Rosa: Author's Publishing Cooperative, 2007.

Heller, Rachel and Levine, Amir. Attached. The New Science of Adult Attachment and How it Can Help You Find and Keep Love. New York: Penguin Random House, 2010.

Holmes, Peter. The Energetics of Western Herbs: Treatment Strategies Integrating Western and Oriental Herbal Medicine. vol. 1 & vol. 2. Boulder: Snow Lotus Press, 1989.

Kaminski, Patricia and Katz, Richard. Flower Essence Repertory: A Comprehensive Guide. To North American and English Flower Essences for Emotional and Spiritual Well-Being. Nevada City: The Flower Essence Society, 2004.

Kemp, Cynthia. desertalchemy.com

Leggett, Daverick. A Guide to the Energetics of Food, poster, 1995.

MacRitchie, James. Chi Kung: Energy For Life. London: Thorsons/HarperCollins, 2002.

May Gaskin, Ina. Guide to Childbirth. New York: Random House Publishing Group, 2003.

McCartney, Francesca. Body of Health: The New Science of Intuition Medicine for Energy and Balance. Novato, Calif.: Nataraj Publishing, 2005.

McCarver, Dhiresha and Woods, Gary. The Photographic I Ching. New York: Marlowe and Company, 1997.

e, Hugh. The Heart of Listening: A Visionary Approach to Craniosacral Work. vol. 1 &. vol. 2. ley: North Atlantic Books, 1995.

Hanh, Thich. Being Peace, Berkeley: Parallax Press, 1987.

Whitney, Eleanor and Rady Rolfes, Sharon. Understanding Nutrition: Fourteenth Edition. St. West Publishing Company, 2015.

hman, James. Energy Medicine: The Scientific Basis. Edinburgh: Elsevier, 2016.

chford, Paul. Healing with Whole Foods: Oriental Traditions and Modern Nutrition. Berkeley: orth Atlantic Books, 2002.

ert, Candice. Molecules of Emotion: The Science Behind MindBody Medicine. New York: Touchstone, 1997.

Porges, Stephen. The Pocket Guide to the Polyvagal Theory: The Transformative Power of Feeling Safe. New York: W.W. Norton and Company, 2017.

Prechtel, Martin. Secrets of the Talking Jaguar: Memoirs from the Living Heart of a Mayan Village. New York: Jeremy P. Tarcher, Putnam Books, 1998.

Prechtel, Martin. Stealing Benefacio's Roses. Berkeley: North Atlantic Books, 2006.

Roslyn, insta post

Selig, Paul. The Book of Mastery, a Channeled Text. New York: Penguin Random House LLC, 2016.

Sills, Franklin. Foundations in Craniosacral Biodynamics: The Breath of Life and Fundamental Skills. Berkeley: North Atlantic Books, 2012.

William, Anthony. Life-Changing Foods: Save Yourself and the One's You Love with the Hidden Healing Powers of Fruits and Vegetables. Hay House Inc., 2016

Wood, Rebecca. The Splendid Grain. New York: William Morrow and Company Inc., 1997.

FOOTNOTES

Chapter 2

1. Achterberg, Jeanne. Creating Integrative Health Care annual symposium San Diego, 1998. Saybrook University Handout, 2006.

2. Ibid

3. Van der Wal, Jaap. Embryology: Where Biology Meets Biography. Embryology Seminar Boulder, Colo. 2003.

4. Sills, Franklin. Foundations in Craniosacral Biodynamics: The Sentient Embryo, Tissue Intelligence and Trauma Resolution. Berkeley, North Atlantic Books, 2012.

5. Rudd, Richard. The Gene Keys, Embracing Your Higher Purpose. London: Watkins Publishing, 2015.

6. Eden, Donna; Feinstein, David. Energy Medicine: Balancing your Body's Energies. For Optimal Health, Joy, and Vitality. New York: Penguin Group, 2008.

7. https://birthpsychology.com/content/about-appah

8. Porges, Stephen. The Pocket Guide to the Polyvagal Theory: The Transformative Power of Feeling Safe. New York: W.W. Norton and Company, 2017.

9. Jarboux, Damaris. Qigong, Anthroposophy and Therapeutic Touch, lecture. Boulder Colo., 2001.

10. https://ehealthlearning.tv/course/protective-qi-and-supporting-the-respiratory-tract/

11. Eden, Donna. Energy Medicine: Balancing Your Body's Energies for Optimal Health, Joy and Vitality. New York: Penguin Group, 2008.

12. Krippner, Stanley. Personal Mythology: An introduction to the concept. The Humanistic Psychologist, (Vo. 18(2), Sum 1990, 137-142).

Chapter 4

1. Andreev, Daniel. The Rose of the World. New York: Lindisfarne Books, 1996.

Chapter 5

1. French, Darcey, IG @sacredearthmedicine

2. Tiller, William. Psychoenergetic Science. Walnut Creek, Calif.: Pavoir, 2007.

3. Prechtel, Martin. Long Life, Honey in the Heart: A Story of Initiation and Eloquence from the Shores of a Mayan Lake. Berkley: North Atlantic Books, 1999.

Chapter 6

1. Sloan, Adrienne. online lecture, Aug. 22, 2020.

2. Eden, Donna; Feinstein, David. Energy Medicine: Balancing your Body's Energies. For Optimal Health, Joy, and Vitality. New York: Penguin Group, 2008.

Made in the USA
Columbia, SC
04 January 2023

75561247R00148